IN SEARCH OF WHOLENESS

A Christian theology of healing and practical training for church and medical settings

Written by Russ Parker
in association with Derek Fraser and David Rivers

Edited by Revd Eileen Turner
and designed by David Payne

Published by St John's Extension Studies
Bramcote, Nottingham NG9 3RL

© St John's Extension Studies and Acorn Christian Foundation, 2000
Revised 2008, 2010

Produced in collaboration with the Leeds Teaching Hospitals Chaplaincy Centre

ISBN 973-1-900920-15-5

Images © iStockphoto.com

Printed in Great Britain by B&B Press Ltd, Rotherham

CONTENTS

Who this book is for

How to use this book

1. THE HOLISTIC VISION OF HEALING   1
The current divide in Christian involvement in healing today, and the importance of bridging the gap between medicine and the church.

2. A THEOLOGY OF HEALING   9
What health means, and how to understand Christ's call to heal the sick in the light of the inevitable death of each of us.

3. ISSUES IN HEALING TODAY   21
A summary of some of the key themes relevant to health and healing that Christians need to be aware of.

4. SKILLED HELPERS   37
The main human skills and personal attitudes that are needed in all those who engage with ill people.

5. VISITING THE SICK   51
The role of the lay visitor in a modern NHS hospital, and their appropriate place in fostering healing in the medical setting.

6. OPEN TO GOD'S TOUCH   69
Playing your part in the healing ministry of the church today, especially in praying with others in the local church context.

7. WORKING IN THE OVERLAP   83
Developing our respect for both the power of medicine and the power of prayer, and knowing where our primary calling lies.

8. HARD QUESTIONS   91
Difficult questions and issues surrounding health and healing today, and some attempts at some answers.

Training to be a Hospital Visitor   105

Training in Prayer for Healing   106

WHO THIS BOOK IS FOR?

This workbook is for Christians who want to be involved in God's gracious healing processes in our world today. You may have a very clear idea of how you want to do this - perhaps by becoming involved in your church's healing services, or by starting such services, or by praying for individuals for healing, or by visiting those who are sick either in their homes or in hospital. All of these can be ways of being instrumental in God's healing purposes. Whatever you think you want to do, we hope that you will approach this workbook with an open mind. We all come to the question of illness and healing from a particular background, with particular experiences in our own lives. However good and powerful these experiences have been, they are seldom the whole picture. Sometimes they even take us in the wrong direction. We may need a better understanding of the purposes of God in bringing healing and wholeness to our lives, before we can see where our particular gifts and abilities fit into those purposes.

That is why we have created a workbook that deals both with the church's healing ministry through prayer and Christian involvement in the world of modern medical treatments. Too often, Christians have a vision for only one of these - and disdain the other, seeing it only as a last resort. So Christians who visit in hospitals often distance themselves from the pursuit of God's miraculous intervention through the prayer and worship of the church. And Christians who find God using them in bringing healing through prayer sometimes discourage people from taking advantage of the healing power of modern medical science.

This workbook is for those who are willing to learn about healing in all its different forms. Although we may be called to serve God in one particular form of healing, it is important that we work with an awareness of the wider picture.

It is also for those who know they want to draw alongside those who are ill and suffering, but are not sure how. We hope that the broad picture of Christian healing given here will help you see your way forward.

Perhaps most of all, this workbook is for those who are willing to minister to individuals across the boundaries of church and hospital. Although there is Christian involvement in both these spheres, there are few Christians who are at home in both.

But individual ill people often make the journey from one setting to another - perhaps because medical science can apparently do little for their condition, or because despite prayers for healing nothing seems to have happened. It can be a lonely journey, as those they leave behind can see their journey as a 'failure' of their sphere of healing, and do not travel with them in search of another way. It is our hope that Christians will learn to make this journey with the ill, and so help them find healing in whatever sphere is appropriate for them within the will of God.

HOW TO USE THIS BOOK

This workbook is more than a book. It is part of a wider training process, designed to help you develop the skills, attitudes and qualities that are important in being a channel of God's healing grace. There are various settings in which this can take place, but the two we have focused on specifically are:

- the role of the lay hospital visitor (alongside the ministry of Hospital Chaplains)
- the role of intercessor for healing within the context of the local church (alongside the ministry of clergy and other church leaders).

So the workbook forms the basis of two different training provisions. It is to be used to train hospital visitors in various hospital settings; this is entirely at the discretion of the hospital chaplains, so check whether the local chaplain is aware of the workbook. It is also to be used in a training course provided jointly by St John's Extension Studies and the Acorn Christian Foundation. More details of these two training schemes can be found at the end of the workbook. You can start working on the material in this workbook before approaching either training setting. Indeed, this may help you decide which area of training to approach first.

But the workbook can also be used more informally. If you find yourself praying with individuals for their healing, then the perspectives in this workbook will help direct your ministry with them. If your church has occasional services in which you offer prayer for for healing, you may want to work through this workbook together to seek to improve your practice. But it would be our recommendation that at least one person from every church setting in which such prayer takes place should take the more formal course. Above all, this workbook is the basis of training and development, not a book to make people more knowledgeable about healing. We urge you to use it in that way.

THE HOLISTIC VISION OF HEALING

PURPOSE

This Unit outlines current attitudes to health and healing in the church and in society, and tries to set the issue of healing within a wider context.

CONTENTS

Mend the gap   2
The cares of this world   4
A time to heal?   6
Healthy – for what?   8

MEND THE GAP

Mention 'healing' to a mixed group of committed Christians today, and it is not difficult to get a lively discussion going.

- A few will have experience of powerful 'healing ministries'. They may have attended healing crusades, and may testify to having seen remarkable miracles.

- More will have at least prayed for themselves or others in special services for healing. They may testify to significant improvements in response to these prayers.

- Some doctors and nurses see their work as continuing Christ's concern for the sick and needy. Often they are positive about prayer for healing, although sceptical about extravagant claims.

- Many will be confused. Even when we are open to God's healing touch, there seems an enormous gap between the healing ministry of Jesus and what we experience today. If Jesus cared for people so much that he healed them with a touch, why is he apparently so reticent to do the same today?

- Some will be doubtful, especially about miraculous healings. God has put healing into our own hands. Christians need to show love and care to the sick, and to support the medical services in the wonderful work they do.

- A few will be openly hostile. Great damage can be done by raising people's hopes, and the church can be guilty of exploiting people's sense of need to boost its own flagging attendance records. The church should do what it knows best – supporting people personally and spiritually, so that they have the courage to live positively through their troubles.

Indeed, a great divide has appeared in Christian involvement in the promotion of health and healing today. In a sense it is the divide between the hospital and the church.

THE POWER OF CARE

Recent years have seen a growing place for 'chaplaincy' in the NHS, and increasing recognition of the broader personal and 'spiritual' aspects of being healthy.

- Some illnesses seem to be affected by the inner state of the person. The progression of some cancers is significantly retarded in those who decide to 'fight' them, while those who 'bow to the inevitable' can die very quickly.

- Other illnesses again seem in part to be caused by inner factors, and seem intractable without addressing personal and social issues.

Thus there has been a rise in the number of hospital chaplains, and increasing demand for their services. Chaplains are now part of the 'health team', resourcing patients and staff. Many chaplaincies can only meet the demands on them through their team of volunteer 'visitors', many of them Christians from local churches. Local GP surgeries have also begun to employ counsellors or simply 'listeners', to address the needs of those whose ailments are largely personal. Again many Christians have become involved in such care.

Such care is generally seen as a wonderful testimony to the love of God. Christians have been in the forefront of medical work and research, confident of God's desire that we should be well. We have abjectly handed over this area of work to the secular structures of our society, but it is an integral part of the working out of God's kingdom purposes.

The power to heal is in our hands, although we can rely on God to play His part.

THE POWER OF PRAYER

Recent years have also seen a huge resurgence in prayer for healing. This has had a widespread affect.

- from charismatic to high church
- from cathedrals to rural churches
- from emotional and sensational events to quiet prayers for healing
- from general prayers for 'needs' to specific words of knowledge

It is now common to believe that God brings healing to people today – usually in small and quiet ways but sometimes in more dramatic forms – and that we are all called to continue to pray for healing even when it seems slow in coming. Jesus healed; we now have his Spirit within us; Jesus promised we would do even greater things than he did; so we are only limited by our own lack of faith.

Such healing is generally seen as a wonderful testimony to the power of God. If people have stopped going to church because the church is irrelevant and God seems remote, here is a way of putting God back on the agenda. God really does care about people, and here's the proof – at least for those who are open to it.

The power to heal is in His hands, although we are also called to play our part.

THE HEART OF HEALING

If you have experienced healing in response to prayer, can you find one word which expresses the core element of that healing? You might think of: freedom, salvation, love, peace, forgiveness.

As you reflect on your experience, move the fulcrum of the sea-saw below to show where you think the balance lies in healing between care and cure.

care   cure

This workbook is an attempt to mend the gap

Among some Christians there is an unfortunate sense of competition with 'secular' medicine, sometimes counselling those who come for prayer to look to God *rather than* medicine to cure their illnesses.

Among other Christians there is a sad suspicion about any confident anticipation of the healing power of God in response to our prayers, sometimes counselling those who are ill to look to modern medicine *rather than* pray to God to restore them to health.

There are dangers in both these approaches in isolation. Their critics see them all too clearly. But it is our conviction that health is found in the overlap between what we can do for ourselves and what God is willing and able to do for us beyond our abilities – even beyond our expectations.

CARES OF THIS WORLD

In this third millennium health is one of the most important issues to occupy modern society. Many people are prepared to spend serious money, time and energy on keeping fit, whether in the gym or at home with a glamorous DVD. Leisure centres report capacity use of their facilities. We are very optimistic about being well and staying well. We are even optimistic about staying young, and many middle-aged people dread the thought of growing old, let alone of death itself. For our society, the key to life is health.

THIS WORLDLY

We live in a society preoccupied with this world. We are taught to believe what we can see, and trust in what we can touch and test. For many, their life consists in the abundance of their possessions, and in a healthy body with which to enjoy them. We put significant effort into making life safe and comfortable. Increasingly we take measures to preserve the environment, so that our children – and then their children – can enjoy this same quality of life. Since this world is all there is, this is the greatest thing we can do for them.

It was not always like this. We used to have a lively sense of a spiritual world, of spiritual realities which impinged on the world we can see and touch. If anything, *this* was the real world, the realm of things that lasted, the arena of life in which justice was eventually done and things finally made sense. Even in traditional Greek thought, upon which most Western philosophy is based, this present world is like shadows cast by the solid realities that we never see. Once you had the faith to trust in things beyond this present world, you were at last on solid ground.

In a sense this shift in attitude is understandable. Setting your heart on another world was partly the product of an unpleasant experience of life in this one. As industrialisation, science and medicine have brought a higher quality of life to the Western world, the attraction of believing

in another world has receded. If this world can be made into a kind of paradise, then why wait for another one? If the 'fallenness' of this world can be reversed, why continue to hope for a new world?

But the shift has changed the way we approach many things, including health.

- **We are determined to be well.** If this life is all there is, then 'being well' in it is hugely important. Sickness cannot simply be borne, in the knowledge of a better life beyond. Thus people take great interest in their health, and many become quite knowledgeable about it. Doctors sometimes complain that patients now arrive in their surgeries complete with their initial diagnosis of what is wrong with them!

- **We need to do it.** If there is no spiritual world impinging on this one, *you* have to make the changes necessary for better health. Indeed the experience of doing this has been a good one. Modern medicine, and especially the advent of the NHS, has rolled back the tide of disease – to such an extent that many people now feel unfortunate if they contract any serious condition.

- **We can deliver it.** Health has become 'industrialised', turned into a product that can be packaged and provided to large numbers of people at affordable cost. It is part of the pervading market economy, with providers and customers – and with complaints and litigation when the product is not up to standard. Part of the crisis in the NHS is the loss of sense of vocation amongst staff, amid the pressures of working within the 'market' setting.

BEING AN INDIVIDUAL

We also live in a society preoccupied with the individual. At worst this is a kind of selfishness, pursuing personal happiness and fulfilment regardless of the effects on others. But more widely it is looking at happiness and fulfilment in very individual ways, and the effects on society and on the environment do not weigh very heavily. This is the context within which many 'rights' movements are currently taking place, and it slants all the issues involved.

Again, it was not always like this. In the various social and cultural contexts within which the Bible was written, there was a strong sense of community – even with those who are dead and with those who are not yet born. It was the well-being of the social group or the extended family that mattered. Thus it was entirely logical for individuals to make significant personal sacrifices to secure this, including extreme suffering and death. A similar attitude to society has pervaded most of human history.

In a sense this change was again a good thing. Social and political realities can crush individuals – even ones which set out to champion the cause of the downtrodden, as the Soviet experiment discovered. If family and community are *all that matter, then a terrible fate can befall individuals who do not serve its purposes.*

But it also slants everything, including our attitude to health.

- **Health care is about treating individuals.** The medical system talks about 'the patient' – almost as if they are disconnected from the people and the environment that surround them. As specialisation draws doctors and researchers into narrower and narrower fields of medical practice, the individual is often not seen as a whole. Despite the reaction to this in the rise of 'holistic' alternative therapies, this narrow focus is still typical of modern medical care.

- **Unwell individuals are victims.** Once we no longer see our health as part of a wider set of problems within society, the question arises, 'Why me?' Thus people feel that life has dealt with them unfairly if they 'happen' to contract a serious disease. In their anger against this injustice, they can seek out who is to blame, even who should be sued. There is a strong sense of 'not deserving' whatever measure of ill-health comes our way, and no sense of corporate responsibility for the way things are.

A TIME TO HEAL?

This emphasis on the here and now, and on individual well-being, is the context within which the church today is called to live the life of faith, to stand in the line of those who in the past have believed and trusted in God (see Hebrews 11). It is a context which offers us great opportunities to proclaim and live out a Christian approach to health and healing, and through that to demonstrate the saving grace of God in ways that our society can understand and identify with.

In particular, the church is called to testify to two truths, to balance the spirit of our age:

More than this world

Life is more than what we see and experience in the physical world. Like Abraham, we are all called to be on the move, engaged with the present world but always aware that the fulfilment of our hope in Christ relies also on the existence of spiritual realities. These impinge on our present world, and will in the end outlast it.

Indeed, Christian faith sees the whole of our life in this world as a journey, and invites us to experience it as such. There is no arriving. It is a journey towards health and wholeness (among other things). There will be great encouragements and achievements along the way, but if our heart is set on arriving – on being wholly well – we will always be disappointed.

More than just me

The purpose of life in this world is the creation of a new humanity, a new community. The biblical pictures of the life beyond this one are all communal – the kingdom, the new Jerusalem, and so on. Our central hope is not for the renewed individual, but for a just and generous society which those who are willing to live under its regime are invited to join. Certainly we will need to be renewed to be able to do this, but such individual renewal is not the ultimate goal.

A MIXED PICTURE

Sadly the church has only been partially faithful to these callings.

- It has often been functioning in 'survival' mode, focusing on keeping up its physical and visible presence.

- It has been greatly influenced by the individualism of today, with the emphasis on individual spiritual journeys and solitary witness to Christian faith wherever the individual finds themselves.

Amid these and other pressures, the church in recent centuries lost its belief in the healing power of God breaking into our world to further His purposes. At the beginning of the 20th century healing was regarded with suspicion by the mainstream churches and had not featured as a normal part of its liturgies and ministries for over 400 years.

Alongside this partial failure of the church have been spiritual and social movements in society, especially the New Age. People have sensed that a society made up of individuals and focused merely on physical realities is not fully human. Thus we have seen the rise of alternative therapies, many of which have a spiritual dimension and a 'holistic' approach to health, looking at the individual within their wider social and physical environment.

MORE THAN CURED

Jesus healed people of physical disabilities. The Gospels are full of stories of him healing the blind, helping the lame to walk and cleansing the lepers.

However the stories do not end there, and sometimes do not even start there. In Luke 17 Jesus is walking in the border region between Samaria and Galilee, where there is tribal strife and community breakdown. A group of ten lepers is suddenly divided when they are healed, because one of them is a Samaritan and cannot go with the others to the temple to have his healing confirmed. By healing, Jesus exposed these racial tensions.

The real focus of Christian healing is not merely curing the physical or emotional problems we suffer from. It is an invitation to go on a journey into wholeness with God, where the richness of His care is nurtured to the roots of our being and our relationships.

Even in mainstream medicine there is currently a renewed interest in the 'spiritual'. In 1996 professional health care workers staged a Body and Soul Conference where spirituality in health care was thoroughly debated and explored. The media interest was such that the conference was repeated the following year and the contents published.

But the 20th century also saw a renewal of Christian concern for healing. This began with the Guild of St Raphael, the Guild of Health and the Divine Healing Mission. The Archbishops of Canterbury and York appointed their first ever Adviser on Healing (Morris Maddocks). And in 1985 the profile of healing in the UK was raised significantly by John Wimber – mostly within charismatic circles but across all the denominations. Today many Anglican churches have some form of healing service as part of their ministry. The current Adviser on Healing is Revd Beatrice Brandon.

A NEW INITIATIVE

It was in response to this rising Christian involvement in health and healing that the House of Bishops commissioned the report **A Time to Heal**. Published in 2000, this was the first comprehensive investigation of Christian healing by the Church of England in over 40 years. It signals that the practice of prayer for healing is back on the agenda of the church, and makes wide-ranging recommendations aimed at ensuring this ministry is both safer and more effective.

Among its various recommendations, there are three particular emphases:

- **A call to take healing seriously.** Despite the advances in Christian healing ministries, the church is still too reticent about this aspect of its ministry. Involvement in health and healing is an important 'cutting edge' between the church and society. Every church ought to find an appropriate expression of this aspect of Christian truth.

  The power of Jesus wielded for the redemption of sins and the healing of lives is the same power that the Church believes it wields today. ... There is no way around this belief. (A Time to Heal page 21).

- **A call to see the wider picture.** The report is clear that there is a spiritual dimension to the whole of life, including health. God has purposes in this world which go beyond its boundaries. We must look for meaning in life on a wider frame of reference than the present age. Thus both healing and suffering have their place.

  Unless the ministry of healing is exercised under the cross, it is not the healing ministry of Christ. ... Our identity is being forged in the crucible of whatever sufferings turn out to be inextricable from the particular journey of each person, and of us together, into the fullness of life. (A Time to Heal pages 23, 128)

- **A call to restore relationships.** Christian faith declares that the essential component of human well-being is the healing of the relationship with God, and then the healing of our other relationships. These reconciliations are the greatest healings and the greatest miracles. We must look for the healing of the body and the mind alongside these greater realities.

  What God desires most of all is our ever closer relationship with him, which may include a deeper share in the sufferings of Christ. ... This love is a call to action and that action will speak of relationship. Perhaps valued relationships matter more than results. (A Time to Heal pages 14, 129)

> **How come you know Jesus and you no heal nobody?**
> **A Sioux Indian Christian**

> **Medicine owes its greatest debt not to Hippocrates, but to Jesus. Without His Spirit, medicine degenerates into depersonalised methodology, and its ethical code becomes a mere legal system.**
> **J W Provonsha MD**

HEALTHY – FOR WHAT?

Viktor Frankl was a psychiatrist who was imprisoned in a Second World War concentration camp. Some survived this demanding ordeal, while others sadly did not. Frankl was one who did – perhaps because he busied himself in a study of why some did survive the ordeal. It was not only a question of physical strength, or even emotional or personal toughness. It was what he called the 'noogenic' – the sense of meaning or purpose that someone had in their life. Those who had a sense of significance about their lives, who lived by a strong sense of values rather than living only for comfort and happiness, were more likely to remain alive when faced with discomfort and ill-treatment.

After the war, Frankl developed a psychiatric practice that drew on these insights:

> By escape into the mass, man loses his most intrinsic quality: responsibility. On the other hand, when he shoulders the tasks set him by society, man gains something – in that he adds to his responsibility. (Frankl)

By helping patients to a sense of purpose in life, he gave them a reason to get better.

Health for its own sake is not in the end all that healthy. Healing is

> the restoration of the possibility of fulfilling the purpose for which we were created. (A Time to Heal page 129)

This wider picture is an important element in the Christian approach to health and healing. It is the willingness to be caught up into something bigger and beyond ourselves and even our world.

LIKE A SCHOOL?

Perhaps life is rather like an isolated boarding school. Certainly it has a life of its own, and it is important that the experience of being a pupil there is a positive and 'healthy' one. In a good regime, discipline (though perhaps tough) is fair, and pupils enjoy some freedom and recreation alongside an emphasis on academic achievement.

But once the school comes to believe that school life is all there is – that there is nothing beyond school – then everything begins to change. Why put effort into lessons at all – except insofar as people enjoy them? Why develop strength of character? Suddenly most of school life becomes meaningless.

Believing in life beyond school doesn't mean that the quality of life in the school doesn't matter – indeed, being able to regulate that quality of life is itself an important preparation for the future. But it puts school life into a wider context, within which a measure of discomfort, rigour and even pain have their place.

The maximisation of 'feeling good' eventually collapses in on itself. How good is good, and how healthy is healthy? (Like how rich is rich?). Expectations increase exponentially, and people bear minor illnesses with less grace than many have borne great suffering.

The NHS is facing a crisis of expectations which cannot be met. Christians have an opportunity to set human health within a wider context – if they are willing to work in the overlap between health-care and the church.

WHERE TO?

Compare Mary Magdelene's encounter with the risen Christ (John 20:10-18) with Thomas' (John 20:24-31). Why do you think Jesus refused to let Mary touch him, but positively encouraged Thomas to do so? See page 13 for some ideas.

A THEOLOGY OF HEALING

PURPOSE

This Unit outlines some of the essential
teaching of the Bible about healing. If our
healing ministry is to be truly Christian, it
must be faithful to its roots in the Christian
scriptures.

CONTENTS

The meaning of health	10
Shalom: peace on earth	12
The ministry of Jesus	14
Early church experience	16
Death: friend or enemy?	18
Making sense of suffering	20

THE MEANING OF HEALTH

TOO NARROW?

The meaning of 'health' is constantly being hijacked. Doctors, psychologists, sociologists, environmentalists, theologians, politicians – they all narrow it down to their own specialisation. So the idea of health is constantly isolated from its wider context – and the process of healing gets reduced to something very unhealthy!

Christians who are concerned for health and healing must resist the reductionist view of health, and insist on keeping it 'as wide as creation'. But that makes it hard to formulate neat definitions, and we will need to rely on analogies and complementary definitions in order to cover the range of possibilities.

> *Healing is as wide as creation, and is the motive force within it. It must never be narrowed to a part of the whole.*
> *Morris Maddocks*

WELL-BEING

The commandment of God to His chosen people was, 'Be holy, because I am holy' (Leviticus 11:44-45). This was not just about morality. The 'Holiness Code' of Leviticus touches on all aspects of life: physical (like eating habits), social, spiritual and moral. It is a code for overall well-being.

Well-being involves the whole of life – it is 'holistic'. It is not simply a concern for the body – what one writer has termed 'healthism', making physical health a kind of idol. It is not just the feel-good factor of contemporary sociology. And it is not just about spirit and soul. It is all these together. Any one without the others will result in ill-health.

LIFE AT ITS FULLEST

Jesus promised us we would 'have life and have it abundantly' (John 10:10). Here we have a fundamental definition of health – health as a rich **quality of life**, not just the attempt to stay alive for as long as possible.

Greek has two common words for 'life':

- **bios** means being biologically alive, living an upright life, and earning a living.

- **zoë** means life as God has it, life as a principle, life as spiritual and personal.

When John's Gospel speaks of 'eternal life', it is zoë, the quality of life rather than its quantity. And it is a quality of life that starts this side of the grave, during our 'bios'.

This real life, healthy life, abundant life, 'eternal life', is life in relationship. 'This is eternal life, to know the Father and him whom He sent' (John 17:3). Here 'know' means a deep intimate relationship, like Adam 'knew' Eve – it is not just knowing about the Father. Conversely, sickness is a kind of alienation or isolation. 'It is not good (not healthy, we might say) for man to be alone' (Genesis 2:18). In an age of individualism and scientific medicine, isolated people have life in all its quantity. This is not health as God means it to be.

HEALTH AS RECONCILIATION

If real life is life in relationship, healing is the process by which relationships are restored. This is the painstaking and demanding task of forgiveness and reconciliation. Such healing can take place between people and God, between individuals, within communities and families, and between communities.

JUST A PRODUCT?

The contemporary obsession with health begs all kinds of questions. It focuses on making the body beautiful, through aerobics, body-building and other 'health' activities, and promises long life. It has become a product, marketed within a consumer society, available to those who can afford it. This consumer mentality is one of the most unhealthy facts of modern society.

In biblical understanding, health is a process, not a product. It is a journey towards maturity, not a spectacular event. A rich young man asked Jesus, 'What must I do to get – to obtain, to procure – eternal life.' But abundant life is not a product to be procured.

So we can see the reconciliation between Joseph and his brothers (Genesis 45:3-15) as a kind of healing. It didn't just put the family back together again; it involved the transformation and healing of deep-rooted enmities. That family acquired a 'wholeness' that it never had before.

Some politicians have seen the value and necessity of **healing relationships between nations**. When Tony Blair became Prime Minister, one of his first actions was to send a letter of apology to the Irish people for the role of the English government in the infamous potato famine of the 1840s. The letter was greeted with universal applause from all parties in the Republic of Ireland, and it led to Mr Blair being invited to address the Irish Parliament – the first British PM to do so since the founding of the Republic. A similar healing of relationships between whole peoples was facilitated by President Clinton when he apologised to the North American Indians for genocidal policies of white American administrations, and by Queen Elizabeth II when she apologised to the Maori people for the detrimental effects of British imperial rule in New Zealand.

Healing our relationship with God is crucial, because once this is impaired, all the others tend to go wrong. Being reconciled to God is fundamental to health and healing.

Six Hebrew and Greek words, all sometimes translated 'forgiveness', help us understand its meaning:

nasa indicates that a weight has been lifted off

salach means to let go or lift up

kaphar indicates that sin is covered and atonement is made

aphiemi means to let go or send away

exaleipho means to wipe out or wipe away

charidzomai means to be gracious to someone

All these terms convey a generous scenario of healing in which God removes our sins, and in the process relieves us of the burdens (both physical and emotional) that we often carry as a result of them. In sign language the idea of forgiveness is conveyed by wiping the palm of one hand firmly across the other, as if removing any stain and any grievance that may cling to it. Paul writes of a God who wipes away our offences and cancels the unfavourable record of our debts (Colossians 2:13-14).

It is also the invitation for us to do likewise (see 2 Corinthians 5:17-19). When we are the injured party, the Holy Spirit gives us the power to let go of the temptation to live by revenge – and so set the other person free from our anger and resentment. This is never easy, and often needs to be repeated, on a long journey of 'letting go'.

JESUS THE RECONCILER

> **Reconciliation is the most radical form of healing.**
> Mgr Michael Buckley

Reconciliation is central to the work and ministry of Jesus. Through his death and resurrection, he opened the gate to that *quality* of life – eternal life – life in relationship with the Father.

Sometimes physical healing was made possible by the prior healing of forgiveness. In Mark 2:1-12 the paralysed man lowered through the roof is first forgiven. Although it is not explicitly stated, it seems that being forgiven opened him up to the possibility of being restored to wholeness of body too. It is also true that a refusal to forgive can block the road to healing, because our preoccupation with our hurt closes us off from receiving healing. Thus James 5:16 links forgiving one another with praying for one another's healing.

Reconciliation was also central to Jesus' message. The Lord's Prayer can only be prayed by people who forgive each other (Matthew 6:12). The unity of his disciples was essential for the church's witness (John 17:20-24).

MEDICAL RESEARCH

Studies carried out by Manchester University's Department of Psychiatry and the Institute of Psychiatry in London have confirmed that between a fifth and a third of all patients who go to their GP with a physical symptom have no detectable physical illness. Many physical ailments require the healing of a wounded conscience rather than of a damaged organ.

SHALOM: PEACE ON EARTH

The Catholic theologian Hans Kung defines salvation as 'creation healed'. By this he refers not just to the environment, or to the state of world economics, but also to the complex network of relationships within societies. Such global healing is the true purpose of the advent of Jesus Christ.

The World Health Organisation defines health as 'a state of complete physical, mental and social well-being and not merely the absence of disease and infirmity'.

The angels proclaiming the birth of Christ declared the promise of 'shalom (peace) on earth and goodwill to all' (Luke 2:14).

SHALOM

The Hebrew word **shalom** expresses the quality, fullness and well-being of life. Although it is usually translated 'peace', it is the closest Old Testament word for 'health'. Its root meaning is of totality and wholeness, and conveys the concept of the 'good life'. It can also be translated as soundness in life and limb, and wholeness of heart. God's 'peace' is not a kind of therapy. It is the objective declaration of God's loving provision for us.

It may also convey a sacrificial quality of relationships which makes that soundness of life possible. This is reflected in the 'shalom offerings' whereby harmony of relationships is made possible with God and between people (see Exodus 20:24, 24:5, Leviticus 10:14).

Shalom denotes the presence of wholeness, completeness and well-being in all spheres of life – physical, mental and spiritual – and encompasses individual, social and national relationships. It is both personal and political. It extends to the individual's need of health, and to the need for a healthy community and a healthy environment. Peace and healing are frequently set alongside each other (Isaiah 57:19, Jeremiah 14:19), and shalom is what a wounded people need (Jeremiah 6:14).

Implicit in **shalom** is the covenant relationship with God who alone can make such health possible. God is referred to as Yahweh-shalom (Judges 6:24), and one of the names of the Messiah is the prince of shalom (Isaiah 9:6). This 'good life' comes to the world through the story of the people of Israel and through God's covenant promises to His people. It therefore comes to those who receive that covenant and live by its values. For shalom to be enjoyed, God's people need to live the righteous life in obedience to God's law. That is why the 'Law' in the Old Testament becomes such a precious and wonderful thing – it ensures the enjoyment of the good life.

TWO VIEWS

The Hebrew concept of human nature was that we are a psycho-physical unity. What ails one part of our person is bound to impinge upon its other parts. So the psalmist can say (38:3):

> Because of your wrath
>   there is no health in my body;
> my bones have no soundness
>   because of my sin.

The obsessional danger with this was the belief, common in Jesus' day, that your physical problems were the result of your sins. The advantage was that it encouraged the view that health is about tending your relationships as well as giving attention to your diseases.

Contrast this with the Greek idea of a distinct separation between body, soul and spirit. Such a view has influenced the whole of Western thought, and therefore the whole Western Christian tradition. The result was that one aspect of our humanity – the spiritual – was valued at the expense of the others. So people came to believe that the physical was of no real value, whist the spirit and the soul were the real and true quality of the person. The quest for the 'good life' became a private quest for spiritual and personal growth, and openness to the power of God to heal the physical went into decline.

HEALTH IS...

The Hebrew concept of *shalom* invites us to reconsider the horizons of healing which we hold today. We cannot have *shalom* in just one part of our person; if we are seeking 'health' as the Old Testament speaks of it, we must see ourselves as a whole. We must bring our whole selves to God in the search for healing, and gratefully receive the measure of healing we receive in any aspect of ourselves. If we do not always see the physical healing that we desire, that does not mean we are not being healed.

Health is also not a solitary journey. If shalom involves the whole of creation, none of us can be 'well' on our own. The pursuit of health ranges beyond the individual quest to the healing of relationships – between people, between nations, with God.

And health is a journey which stretches beyond this world, because it is ultimately the healing of all creation, for which we look in hope to the coming of our Lord Jesus Christ.

HEALTH AND SALVATION

The Greek *soteria*, usually translated 'salvation', is more correctly translated 'health'. William Tyndale, one of the early translators of the Bible into English, in the story of Zaccheus in Luke 19, translates Jesus as saying, 'Today health has come to this house.' As Christians, wherever we say 'saved', 'salvation' and 'Saviour', we can instead say 'healed', 'health' and 'Physician'.

ANSWERS (from page 8)

For Mary to touch Jesus, it was to receive him back like the former days. Indeed the account is all about her search for Jesus in order to look after him.

For Thomas to touch Jesus, it is a challenge to face his doubts and take the risk of moving forward into the unknown future of growth and service.

No healing, however powerful or miraculous, is intended to take us backwards to how things used to be. It is part of a pathway to a wholeness that we have not yet experienced.

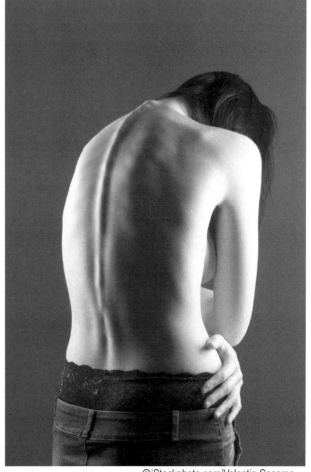

@iStockphoto.com/Valentin Casarsa

THE MINISTRY OF JESUS

Jesus came to initiate a radically new order. He called people to live out a new life-style, obedient to God's purposes for His world, so that God's will would be 'done on earth as it is in heaven'. This was real life, truly human life, with all its potential realised, a quality of life and well-being, as well as a quantity of life in immortality. Such a life-style would be healthy in every respect.

Jesus called this God's 'Kingdom', God's regime. And to enter this regime, Jesus called his hearers to repent and to believe in the good news of this new creation. He challenged them to be reconciled to God and to each other – to be saved, to be 'healed'.

> **Health is ultimately about being truly and fully human, as Jesus was.**

When people are reconciled to God and to each other, life on earth begins to reflect the life of the Godhead, three persons in community, holy and therefore healthy.

NOT JUST WORDS

The two bewildered disciples on the road to Emmaus referred to Jesus as 'a prophet mighty in *deed and word*' (Luke 24:19). The mighty works Jesus did ('signs' as they are described in John's Gospel) were pointers to the coming Kingdom (see Luke 11:20). They were also a foretaste of all that the Kingdom would bring.

SIGNS OF LIFE

John's Gospel is the most explicit in seeing the miracles of Jesus as bringing a fuller and richer quality of life. John's first 'sign' is in fact not a 'healing' at all, but turning water into wine – ordinary life made richer. Subsequent signs release people from bondage and paralysis into a fuller life: the lame man, the official's dying son, the man born blind.

The climax of John's signs is the raising of Lazarus from the dead (John 11), with its long dialogue with Lazarus' sisters about the life that is to come.

So when John the Baptist in prison asks for assurance that Jesus is the promised messiah, Jesus tells the messengers to report to John what they see happening – that Isaiah's prophecies of a healed creation are being fulfilled around them (Luke 7:18-23, Isaiah 35:5-6).

When Jesus sends out his disciples on their first mission, he instructs them to *preach* that the Kingdom is arriving, and to *demonstrate* that it is, by healing, raising the dead and removing demons (Matthew 10:8, Luke 9:2). These miracles are not intended to be spectacles. They are signs that the preaching is true – that the Kingdom is arriving, and that abundant and healthy life is open to those who are reconciled to God and to each other.

NOT ALONE

Although Jesus acted alone in his healing, he had a strong sense of working in partnership with the Father (John 5:19-23). And he sent his disciples out in pairs – as people in community, people in relationship, not as individual superstars.

It is the church, the community of God's people, that inherits the promise of Jesus that his disciples will do greater works than he did (John 14:12). The Holy Spirit is given to the church to empower us for the work of God's Kingdom – for word and sacrament, for preaching and healing. Jesus gives his disciples power and authority to act in this way, as he had received such authority from his Father (Matthew 28:18).

HEALTH FOR PEOPLE

Jesus did not run a campaign against disease – he healed *people*. Look, for example, at the different ways in which Jesus responded to *blind* people, and write down some of the special characteristics of each situation:

- Matthew 9:27-31

- Matthew 12:22-30

- Mark 8:22-26

- Mark 10:46-52

- John 9:1-11

Jesus treated everyone as an individual, and did not assume that the way of approaching one blind person is the same as another.

HEALTH FOR SINNERS

On at least two occasions, Jesus heals by proclaiming the forgiveness of sins – the healing of the paralysed man at Capernaum (Mark 2) and the man at the pool of Beth-zatha (John 5). It may be that these sicknesses were linked to a sinful life, and that Jesus proclaims absolution and reconciliation with God as an essential ingredient in the healing.

But Jesus is at pains to point out elsewhere that sickness and disease are not necessarily linked to sins in the sick person – against the popular beliefs of his day (see John 9:3). All sin brings dis-ease – it brings in its wake disorder and alienation. But generally Jesus saw no direct link between an illness and the particular sins of the sick person.

HEALTH FOR THE OPPRESSED

Jesus brought healing to a number of people not through praying for healing but through breaking demonic illness within the sufferer. Healing was then a consequence of this deliverance. See Mark 9:14-32 for a good example. Indeed of the thirteen incidents of healing in Mark's gospel, four are accounts of deliverance. Healing linked to deliverance forms one of the core categories of Jesus' ministry. Jesus sent out his disciples to do the same (Luke 9:1-6, 10:17-18), and Peter recalls this aspect of Jesus' ministry in one of his sermons (Acts 10:38). Other examples are the casting out of a dumb spirit (Luke 11:14), a deaf and dumb spirit with apparent epileptic fits (Mark 9:14-29), a blind and dumb spirit (Matthew 12:22), and a spirit of infirmity (Luke 13:11-13).

People question whether such accounts are simply another way of describing what we would call 'psychological disturbance' today. But Matthew 4:24 distinguishes between 'the demonised' and 'those having seizures' – the latter being the standard word of the day for 'lunacy'. This gospel writer seems to recognise different origins for the problems of the spiritually oppressed and the psychologically disturbed, even though the symptoms can appear similar.

A MEANS OF CALLING?

Jesus never healed someone and then called them to follow him as a close disciple. Indeed, he sometimes specifically refused an offer to follow him. Instead, he frequently told people who were healed to go back to their ordinary lives. What can we learn from this?

EARLY CHURCH EXPERIENCE

Healing features prominently in the ministry of Jesus, and forms the credentials of the Messiah for the benefit of the imprisoned John the Baptist (Luke 7:18-23). But it does not have the same central place in the book of Acts and is given even less attention in the epistles. Some people have concluded from this that healing was no longer of importance in the early church, and that preaching and witness are the real tasks of the church – then and today.

But it is important to understand the nature of these other New Testament writings. The Acts of the Apostles was written in order to account for the establishment and growth of the Christian church, and the epistles in the main were written to enable believers to grow in faith and holiness.

THE WITNESS OF ACTS

Acts actually records a wide range of healings, largely through the prayers of the apostles Peter and Paul.

- Peter and John healed a lame man at the gate Beautiful on their way to prayers (3:1-10)

- Even Peter's shadow brought healing to many, who were brought out into the street (5:15-16)

- Philip's preaching was accompanied by widespread healing and the removal of unclean spirits (8:4-7)

- Ananias restored Paul's sight after his Damascus Road encounter with the risen Christ (9:17-19)

- Paul healed a crippled man at Lystra (14:8-11)

- Like Jesus, Paul cast out demons – from a fortune teller (16:16-18)

- Even contact with Paul's handkerchief brought healing and freedom from evil spirits (19:11-12)

- Paul also raised the dead – Eutychus at Troas (20:9-12)

- Healings continue right to the end of the Acts, as Paul heals Publius' father on the island of Crete (28:8)

So although healing is less prominent in Acts than in the gospels, healing was an important element in the life of the New Testament church. Such healing was a significant part of the 'signs and wonders' which demonstrated the truth of the Christian gospel (2:43, 5:12-15, 14:3).

THE FOCUS OF THE EPISTLES

Within the epistles, there is no mention of the casting out of demons or of raising the dead. The focus is not on the preaching of the Christian gospel to unbelievers, with its signs following, but on the internal life of the Christian community.

- There is discussion of how the 'gifts' of the Spirit, including that of healing, are meant to work within the fellowship of believers (e.g. 1 Corinthians 12). This is a different setting from healings in relation to gospel preaching, and the transition was causing problems. However we understand the functioning of spiritual gifts, it is clear that the healing of the sick continued as part of the general expectation of what the Christian life was like.

- The subject of healing was dealt with as part of the wider need for good relationships within the fellowship of the church, and between the individual and God. This forms the focus for Paul's teaching on the Lord's Supper, where a lack of spiritual attitude and of care for others was the underlying cause of some illnesses within the church (1 Corinthians 11:27-34). Paul maintains that the healing of personal pain and wounded relationships must be achieved through forgiveness, not through excessive discipline (2 Corinthians 2:5-11).

- Some sicknesses did not respond to prayer – such as Paul's 'thorn in the flesh' (2 Corinthians 12:7-10), and Timothy who was frequently unwell (1 Timothy 5:23).

Paul sees his condition as bringing other, more spiritual, benefits to him; and he reconciles himself to counselling Timothy to take practical measures to help his ailments. But such things are written within a general expectation that those who are unwell would be healed – such as Epaphroditus who nearly died but God had mercy on him (Philippians 2:27). When faced with continuing suffering and sickness, they, like us, struggled to reconcile this with the knowledge of God's ability and willingness to heal.

HEALTH NOT HEALING

The other major New Testament reference to healing comes in James 5:13-18. This is an interesting insight into the normal practice of early church leaders, who prayed for healing using a combination of anointing, confession and prayer. While the elders pray and anoint, there is a general exhortation for everyone to confess their sins to one another in order for the prayers of the church to be effective. A growing lack of openness between Christians was apparently felt to be stemming the flow of the healing power of God.

The use of oil suggests both a medical and a religious purpose. Olive oil was often rubbed into wounds to soothe and cleanse the damaged parts, and was a normal practice in the physician's care of the sick. Anointing of course had religious significance in the Old Testament, and formed part of the healing practice of the disciples when sent out by Jesus (Mark 6:13).

So it seems that, outside the context of the 'signs' that accompanied the preaching of the gospel, the health of the Christian community was pursued by all appropriate means. Both physical and non-physical methods are recommended and employed in the name of the Lord. The power of God to heal is not side-lined, but re-focused in a new context. The Christian community knew that God wanted them to be well, but they also knew from the teaching of Jesus himself that it was a sin to seek for signs (Matthew 12:38-39). Within their own number, therefore, they used all appropriate skills, knowledge and gifts for the healing of their sick, using them all in the name of the Lord of the church.

@iStockphoto.com/Peter Garbet

NOTES

DEATH: FRIEND OR ENEMY?

From time immemorial, death has both fascinated and threatened us. It seems to spell the end of all that a person has become, and yet the idea that perhaps it is not after all the end has frequently intrigued and haunted humanity.

For the Christian healing ministry to remain authentic, it must come to terms with the fact that some people are not healed, others suffer greatly, many are disabled, and all grow old and will one day die. We need a theology of healing that takes into account the reality of death.

OT PERSPECTIVE

The Old Testament has no clear theology of death, but death is seen as the loss of vitality, a reduction to living like a shadow rather than as a real person. The person who dies is described as water being poured out on the ground – impossible to gather up again (2 Samuel 14:14). The underworld is known as 'sheol' where there is no real life, no praise of God and where the dead have no memory of the living (Psalm 6:5).

There is an ambivalence about death in the Old Testament. On the one hand death means being cut off from the presence of God. On the other hand death is something that God brings, an activity of God parallel to bringing life (1 Samuel 2:6, Psalm 90:3-5). Death is seen as a sign of God's judgement on our sins (Genesis 2:17, 3:19), and yet death at a ripe old age can be faced positively if the circumstances are good. Thus Jacob dies content to have seen Joseph alive again (Genesis 46:30), and Joseph dies sensing that his descendants face a good future and ensuring his bones go with them (Genesis 50:24-26).

So death is accepted as a natural event but with a dark side. It can rob people of life prematurely; and because the presence of God is seen very much within the history of Israel in this life, death removes you from that history and puts you on the sidelines. Death wipes away so much that is good.

There are only very vague hints in the Old Testament about the possibility of a positive life after death. Job may have sensed some 'healing' of his various miseries beyond his death (Job 19:25), and Daniel 12:2 speaks of those who sleep in the dust awakening to everlasting life. But the focus of salvation in Old Testament theology is firmly set within the present age. If God does not bring us His salvation in this life, He has abandoned us.

TURN-AROUND

Doubtless Jesus shared this view of death. He brought back to life some who had died prematurely, allowing the widow of Nain's son to return to look after his mother (Luke 7:15), and returning Lazarus to the fellowship of his sisters (John 11). He wept in the garden of Gethsemane as he faced his own impending death, and placed his traumas over it into the hands of his Father.

But the resurrection of Jesus puts all that into new perspective. The Father chose to vindicate His Son by bringing him into a glorious new life after his ignominious death. In the New Testament death is viewed almost exclusively through the window of Christ's resurrection. Death is robbed of its ultimate destructive power, and no longer has the final victory over life. It is no longer the 'last word' even of a long and happy life. So Paul can say that Christ has taken the 'sting' out of human existence, because death is 'swallowed up' as we enter the resurrection life (1 Corinthians 15:54-55).

The first Adam is no longer the prototype of human death. Rather, the experience of Jesus as the second Adam is now the prototype for the death of every human person. Death may still be a challenge, but Jesus has robbed death of its power to terrorise and destroy us.

ON A KNIFE-EDGE

A Christian view of death turns on our belief in the resurrection of Jesus. We are mortal and we must all face our death. We are invited to live life to the full in the here and now but, without a resurrection like that of Jesus, all we have lived will be swept away. However, if in Jesus we have an even greater life beyond our death, then this 'sweeping away' is defeated and the fear of death is turned upside down. Thus faith in Jesus becomes crucial – it is literally a matter of life and death.

In the Christian healing ministry we live on a knife-edge. Death is the opposite of life; illness if unchecked can easily lead to death, or at least to impaired life. So death, like illness, is to be fought, and life is to be extended where possible. Yet from another perspective death is the greatest healing. It is the doorway into a greater expression of the eternal life we already experience in Jesus. As such, it resolves whatever could not be resolved in this life.

Once even death becomes relative, deprived of its dark finality, then all lesser things also change in proportion. All our miracles of healing, and all our mysteries about why some have suffered and not been healed, are surrendered at the gateway to the fuller life.

The process of coming to terms with this is a journey in itself. The journey into death is learning to live to the full, whatever our physical condition. It is common to describe those suffering from a terminal illness as people who are 'dying'; in fact they are 'living' – often with a quality and with a focus that eludes most of the healthy.

SO WHY BE HEALED?

Healing is that which enables us to live the Jesus quality of life. It is a quality of life in relationship with God which begins in the present and extends into eternity.

It is useful to reflect on the raising of Lazarus after he had been dead for four days – perhaps the most spectacular of Jesus' miracles (John 11). This 'healing' brought joy to his sisters who mourned his death, and Lazarus became a minor celebrity. But it also aroused enormous hostility among the chief priests, and Lazarus' new life was immediately in danger (12:9-11). And of course the day would anyway come when Lazarus would age and die, and *not* be raised. Which was the more important experience: the one which restored Lazarus to his family for a few years, or the one which eventually took him into eternity with God?

What do we want from our healing? Is it simply the opportunity to get back to life as it used to be? Or is it our desire to live a fuller and richer life in fellowship with Christ? The gospel is the call to live the kingdom quality of life, and much of this can be done no matter what measure of sickness or health is ours.

@iStockphoto.com/Clint Spencer

MAKING SENSE OF SUFFERING

One thing we cannot – dare not – escape in the ministry of healing is the mystery of suffering. Suffering stands as a challenge to all we believe and expect of God in healing.

The life and ministry of Jesus Christ is the essential clue to the healing of our personal lives, the family, the corporate life of society, and of the nations of the world.

It is worth noting that in Scripture sickness and suffering are not the same thing. References to sickness are mostly to do with the weaknesses and infirmities of the body inherent in our fallen world. References to suffering are mostly to do with persecution (including physical pain) and the afflictions we carry from hostile encounters with others (like being hounded out of our home). 1 Peter contains a lot of teaching about suffering – a letter written in the midst of persecution.

The New Testament is very positive about God's power to heal sicknesses. But even Jesus himself is very forthright about the suffering that his disciples can expect (Luke 21:12-19). The Christian faith does not promise relief from all suffering, and we should not conduct a healing ministry as if it does.

QUESTIONING ASSUMPTIONS

When Jesus healed the man born blind (John 9) he also challenged contemporary opinions about suffering. He made it clear that this man's suffering was not caused by sin – either his or his parents'. Indeed he did not give an alternative explanation for the origins of suffering, and only pointed to the opportunity of using the situation to bring glory to God.

The book of Job is full of questions about where suffering comes from. It too challenges the assumption that Job's suffering is the result of a sinful life or the punishment of God upon sinners. This extreme case is portrayed as a contest between Satan and God, although this is never revealed to Job.

CHRIST THE MODEL

Jesus suffered. He was rejected and misunderstood throughout a lot of his life. There is no evidence he was immune from sickness himself, and he refused to use his power to relieve his own pain and discomfort (Luke 4:2-4, 4:23, 23:35-37).

But because Jesus was 'tested by what he suffered' (Hebrews 2:18), he becomes the one who can sustain us during our times of suffering and testing. Indeed, through the incarnation and sufferings of Christ, suffering becomes a vehicle through which the saving and healing presence of God can become available to us. He is also the pioneer of what we will all experience – he has already come through all his sufferings and entered ahead of us into the new life.

Thus the resolution of the mystery of suffering does not lie in this world alone. Paul paints a clear picture of a new creation, which will be brought into being precisely through the 'birth pains' of the present age (Romans 8:18-23). The idea of another world is not escapism – there is no escaping these pains – it is a realistic picture of how the Christian hope in a living and loving God can be fulfilled. It is based on the model of Jesus, whose resurrection has brought him into that new life ahead of us, by a kind of 'shortening' of the time line. Our hope lies ultimately not in relieving suffering now (although that should be done) but in the whole-scale renewal of creation.

ISSUES IN HEALING TODAY

PURPOSE

This Unit gives a broad outline of some of the major issues that Christians need to understand if they are to be involved in bringing greater health and healing to those who are ill.·

CONTENTS

A bit of history   22
Medicine and prayer   24
What about miracles?   26
The question of demons   28
Dealing with death   30
Losing – and winning   32
Alternatives old and new   34

A BIT OF HISTORY

The development of the Christian healing ministry had a chequered history following the Apostolic period.

EARLY DECLINE

Certainly healing continued to form one of the main platforms for the conversion of the Roman Empire during the next 300 years. The most influential factor in the conversion of the Empire to the Christian faith was not apologetics or formal evangelism but the power to heal – because this convinced a pagan society that God was present in the church (see Ramsay MacMullen, *Christianizing the Roman Empire*).

This is confirmed in the writings of the early Fathers: Irenaeus (in *Adversus Omnes Haereses*) claimed that heretics did not have access to the power of God, which was why they were unable to heal.

However, by the beginning of the fourth century, Cyprian, the Bishop of Carthage in North Africa, was complaining that the healing ministry lacked strength in prayer because the church was growing more worldly. The Edict of Milan in 313, which recognised the legitimacy of the Christian faith within the Roman Empire, proved to be something of a watershed in the spiritual vitality of the Church. Part of this was a decline in the practice of healing through prayer. This was despite the fact that some of the leading theologians of this period (such as Ambrose, Augustine, Basil and Gregory of Nazianzus) believed in the church's commission to practise healing; the latter two also had some knowledge of the medicines of their day.

From this period until the early 20th century, the practice of prayer for healing was focused through individual saints and their associated shrines.

NEW THINKING

A major shift was going on in theological thinking. The more open and spiritual universe of Platonic thought was being superseded by the closed universe and rationalism of Aristotelian thinking. The belief in the miraculous became associated with superstition. The focus became ensuring a good life in the next world, rather than healing in the present age. The practice of anointing for healing took on a whole new existence as 'extreme unction' – preparing the dying for heaven. This change was only reversed in the Catholic church as recently as 1962, when anointing was reinstated as a sacrament for healing.

The decline in the healing ministry was underpinned by a new theological interpretation of healing and suffering. Dispensationalism is the view that God deals differently with people in different eras of history. Applied to the subject of healing, it was thought that the outpouring of healing was a particular manifestation of God's love and power to enable the fledgling church to become established. Once this was accomplished, there was no longer any need for such powerful demonstrations of God's presence. Healing was understood as rather like scaffolding – to facilitate the building of the church, and once completed, it was removed. Healing became something to look forward to beyond death.

Suffering became something to be endured, and came to be viewed as the necessary purging of the body in order to free the spirit to meet with God in eternity.

MORE CARE THAN PRAYER

All this was reflected in the practice of hospitality and care that grew with the rise of monastic communities. Hospitals and infirmaries were founded, where the sick were nursed and treated with natural remedies. The aged and disabled also found shelter and care. The monasteries created herb gardens and applied healing remedies on an empirical basis. There is some evidence that the monasteries also provided a form of 'community care' by visiting the sick in their homes.

But during the Middle Ages the church began to withdraw from the practice of medicine, and by the 12th century monks were forbidden to do so. Astonishingly, in 1123 the First Lateran Council forbade monks to visit the sick in their homes. Medicine became the exclusive work of the professionals. An inter-dependence between the spiritual work of the church and the practices of the medical profession would not be advocated for over 800 years.

THE WITNESS OF THE SAINTS

It was saintly and gifted people who kept the practice of prayer for healing alive. In the Dark Ages there were the Desert Fathers, who so influenced Bishop Martin of Tours. He in turn was an inspiration to Celtic Christianity, in the persons of Columba, Cuthbert, Bridget and Hilda. Bede in his *Ecclesiastical History* notes that the hallmark of these saints was their effectual prayers for healing.

Moving on through history, there is Francis of Assisi. Martin Luther wrote a liturgy for a healing service based on the letter of James. The Society of Friends and the Methodist movement both acknowledged the healing ministry (medical and non-medical) of their founders. John Wesley opened the first free medical dispensary in England for the treatment of the poor. In 1747 he published a book entitled *Primitive Physic, or an Easy and Natural Method of Curing Most Diseases*; it was still in print a century later!

The modern medical missionary movement built on this foundation. By the year 1910 over 2000 hospitals and at least twice that number of health centres were being operated by the missionary agencies of the Protestant churches alone. This grew throughout the 20th century, and was aided by the establishment of the Christian Medical Commission, set up by the World Council in 1968.

REVIVAL

The 20th century witnessed a revival of broad church involvement in Christian healing. Various Guilds were formed to bring teaching and resources to the churches. These included the Guild of Health, the Guild of St Raphael, the Divine Healing Mission, the Order of St Luke, and latterly the Acorn Christian Healing Foundation. The Church of England debated healing at various Lambeth Conferences, and published a Report following the 1958 Conference. The House of Bishops commissioned a new report in 2000, *A Time to Heal*.

In 1947 the British Medical Association approved a statement on medicine and the church:

Medicine and the Church working together should encourage a dynamic philosophy of health which would enable every citizen to find a way of life based on moral principle and on a sound knowledge of the factors which promote health and well-being.

All these initiatives called for a holistic view of healing, which saw prayer and medicine as partners in the care of the whole person, and not as rivals. In contrast, the mushrooming of healing ministries in churches touched by charismatic renewal has emphasised miraculous healing and there has been little encouragement to collaborate with medicine.

SHRINES

Connected with the lives of the saints were shrines where their powers were still available for the needy. Relatively modern healing shrines have emerged at Lourdes in France, Fatima in Portugal, Walsingham in England, and Knock in Ireland. In their own way they have signalled a revival of interest in prayer for healing. With the advent of charismatic renewal in the 20th century, there arose the evangelical shrines of the Airport Church in Toronto, and divine healing crusades (portable shrines…) focused on powerful individuals such as Kathleen Kuhlman, Morris Cerello, Francis MacNutt and John Wimber.

MEDICINE AND PRAYER

Both Christian healing and medical healing come from God, and for Christian people there should be no conflict between them. Going to the doctor and receiving the laying on of hands are not mutually exclusive. You can say your prayers and take your medicine as well. You need to view with suspicion anyone who denies that connection. The physical and the spiritual are connected in all kinds of ways and keep on interacting within us.

Tom Smail

The two caring disciplines of doctor and priest, of hospital and church, are both ministries of God's loving care for the hurting individual. Both can work together, like two people in a marriage caring for their children.

But equally each has a different role to play, and should retain their individuality. Thus a priest may hesitate to speak of medical matters, and a doctor of spiritual matters. It is in fact helpful for the sufferer to receive the Spirit's wisdom through two independent channels, each with their own wisdom and training.

MEDICINE WITHOUT PRAYER

Medical science is a small part of the vast wisdom that God has encouraged and inspired humanity to explore and acquire. It is an objective body of knowledge about the marvels of the human body, without particular spiritual values.

Most doctors and nurses, with or without faith, are highly motivated caring people, who see the patient as a person to be served. They draw on their medical wisdom and experience to do this. The Christian medic draws on this same wisdom, but also sees the patient within the overall perspective of God's yearning for them to be 'whole' in body, mind and spirit.

Some doctors see their medical knowledge as a source of self-congratulation, a thinly veiled exercise of power over others. Medicine can become an idol at whose feet the sick must bow, surrendering their individuality and becoming a 'case' to be treated, a fine exhibit of medical truth. Prayer for healing is seen only as the manipulation of psychosomatic conditions, and where it is apparently effective it is filed away under inexplicable paramedical activity, thus outside the boundaries of the medical profession.

In psychiatry, the genuine vulnerable faith of someone with a disturbed personality is sometimes wrongly perceived as evidence of a weak psyche. In fact, it is a thin but vital lifeline to the eternal truths that undergird the very existence of the patient, the psychiatrist, his wisdom, and all creation. Christian psychiatrists often work against the cynicism of colleagues in taking the spiritual dimension seriously within the mystery of personality.

PRAYER WITHOUT MEDICINE

When James encouraged the early Christians to pray for healing, he advocated anointing with oil in the name of Jesus (James 5:14). Oil was part of the medication of the day, as well as having religious significance. In fact, Christians throughout the ages have generally had a positive attitude to all forms of bringing healing. Many Christians have been involved in the development of medical science, and have pioneered medical practice as part of the work of the Kingdom in far-flung parts of the world.

However, some Christian groups believe that prayer is the only legitimate means of healing. Medical treatment is dismissed as worldly, even sinister. Christians are accused of disobedience if they reject such teaching, and of a lack of faith if they are not miraculously healed. Some Christian leaders, perhaps insecure in their own position, seek to prove that faith can outmatch medical wisdom.

But it is clear that Christians in the early church were sometimes ill, and not always healed. Timothy had 'frequent illnesses', for which Paul suggested he take some wine (1 Timothy 5:23). Trophimus was 'left ill' in Miletus (2 Timothy 4:20). When Paul got ill it provided him with an opportunity to preach the gospel (Galatians 4:13); and he felt the need to mention his famous 'thorn in the flesh', whatever that was (2 Corinthians 12:7-10). So there is no justification for the view that a Christian should never be ill, or that such illness should always be cured.

WORKING TOGETHER

A young Anglican Curate approached a local GP practice boldly and openly, wishing to discuss mutually relevant problems. The doctors were most impressed by his down to earth and practical concerns for his parishioners, and the support that doctors and clergy could give each other soon became apparent. They began meeting regularly for sandwich lunches and discussions, and were soon joined by other clergy. Twenty years on the meetings continue, and many patients have benefited from the combined wisdom of doctors and clergy discussing (with their consent) their personal or family problems.

This situation is not unique. There is often caution and suspicion over doctor/clergy cooperation, often focused on the issue of confidentiality. But in some practices a minister is a key member of the Primary Health Care Team. Sometimes the needs of the local community dictate common areas of concern – for instance, a new council housing estate for young families. If the church is a caring, welcoming and healing community with a well-thought-out caring strategy, there is no need to be apologetic in advertising such resources to the local medical practice.

THE WISDOM OF GOD

Wisdom is of the very essence of God. It is personified in Proverbs (as a woman) as the very first act of God's creative activity (Proverbs 8:22). It is through this Wisdom that our universe was formed, and Wisdom takes special delight in our world and in humanity (Proverbs 8:31).

Christians involved with those who are ill need to draw on the breadth of God's wisdom. They need to respect the wisdom of the doctor and of the priest, the medical and the spiritual. They may be expert in neither, but can stand alongside the ill person and help them integrate these two channels of God's healing touch.

THE MISSION OF BURRSWOOD

Burrswood is a Christian centre for medical and spiritual care. People find the healing of Jesus Christ through skilled nursing, medical expertise, counselling and prayer. Stillness and beauty provide space for the Holy Spirit's transforming work in every area of life. Many who come for a short stay are enabled to do so irrespective of their means.

The community of Burrswood, with its individual gifts and abilities, is committed to bringing together medicine and Christianity and to working within the mystery of healing and suffering. It aims to keep the love of Christ at the heart of care and to be a sign of the Kingdom of God in a hurting world.

WHAT ABOUT MIRACLES?

If we believe that the Church has a ministry of healing, as Jesus did, then it is reasonable to ask whether we are expecting the same sort of 'miraculous' cures as people obviously received at Jesus' hands. If we are, then our scientific age will want to subject any such events to medical scrutiny in a search for evidence for these claims. So we need to be clear about whether events which are 'demonstrably miraculous' are essential to the Christian healing ministry. Those who pray for healing also need to be clear about whether they are expecting the miraculous in response to their prayers; otherwise they may be confused about whether they have had an answer.

NEW TESTAMENT WORDS

There are three Greek words which are all used in relation to healings in the New Testament:

- **dunamis** means 'mighty power' or 'mighty work' (from which we get the word 'dynamite'). It is the explosive force or energy of God, which was at work in the ministry of Jesus (Matthew 11:20, Mark 6:2,5, Luke 19:37). This power is also at work through Philip in establishing the church in Samaria (Acts 8:13), and it characterises the missions of Paul (Acts 19:11). In writing to the church in Corinth, Paul obviously expects that, in addition to gifts of healing, one of the ministry roles will be that of 'doing powerful deeds' (1 Corinthians 12:28). These mighty works may be healings but do not have to be. It is rather the affirmation that there is a power of God available to God's people.

- **semeion** means a 'sign'. It is used extensively in John's Gospel to denote an event which points beyond itself to the death and resurrection of Jesus (John 2:23, 4:54, 6:2). It is used of the healing of the blind man at the gate Beautiful (Acts 4:22), where the apostles are careful to point out that this healing was done in the name of Jesus, and called on those who witnessed it to put their faith in him (4:10-12).

- **teras** is usually translated 'wonder', and is used mostly with *semeion* ('signs and wonders'). In Acts it is used of Jesus and various of the apostles. It indicates something that defies explanation and evokes awe and amazement.

This use of words suggests that the Church should expect God's power to be at work through it, in ways that cannot always be explained and which point beyond themselves to the saving grace of Jesus.

THE MEANING OF MIRACLES

There is a clear tension over miracles in the life of Jesus. On the one hand he accuses people as evil and 'adulterous' for their fascination with the miraculous (Matthew 12:39), and he often encouraged those he healed to keep silent rather than publicise it (e.g. Matthew 9:30). On the other hand, he challenges people to believe in him, if not for his teaching, then for the miracles he had performed (John 10:38).

Throughout the New Testament it seems that miracles were signs for believers and want-to-believers, rather than proof for unbelievers and don't-want-to-believers.

They heralded the kingdom life of God which was coming into the world, rather than drawing attention to the miraculous itself.

- Miraculous healings were confirmations of God's favour amid the suffering of a fallen world (Luke 4:16-21), and a cause for praise (Luke 19:37).

- By contrast, those hostile to Jesus see his miracles either as a sign of Satan's activity, as in the case of the Pharisees (Mark 3:22); or as a further reason to dislike him, as in the reception he received in his home village (Mark 6:5).

WHAT HAPPENS IN MIRACLES?

What is happening when someone is quite miraculously healed? There is a philosophical debate here about whether God interferes with his own creation, or works through it.

The Christian faith proclaims a God who is not distant from His creation like an absentee landlord. He continues to be involved in the history of humanity. But God has a delicate balance to maintain, if He is to see His purposes worked out. If He intervenes too much, He will rob us of the power to choose what we do with our lives. If He never intervenes at all, He has abandoned us to the powers at work in a fallen creation.

Perhaps both the natural and the miraculous are happening when someone is healed in response to prayer. We can see a parallel here to the healing that takes place through surgery or any other treatment of a patient's sickness. A doctor will make an intervention; if it is a good intervention, nature will respond with renewal and healing. This is what any surgeon will say after surgery – they are not the healers, but they facilitate the healing processes which they can see taking place in the body. With prayer for healing, the intervention comes from above, rather than through human skill, but the healing comes through the natural properties of the body.

What seems unique to the ministry of Jesus and the apostles, and extremely rare outside their time, is the instant nature of the healings. Jesus healed with a simple word of command or a touch, and this is rarely the case with the church at prayer. But this is not to deny that God does sometimes choose to intervene today in the process of someone's healing.

ANY EVIDENCE?

The issue of reliable evidence for those claiming miraculous cures is a thorny one. Verification for miracles is notoriously difficult, and where one person may claim a miraculous answer to prayer, a doctor may interpret the same event as a spontaneous remission, quite familiar in his or her experience.

It is true that what is a 'wonder' to one culture and generation may become quite ordinary to another. Chronic blindness can come to be cured by simple surgery; other ailments may respond to 'miracle' drugs and healing soon becomes commonplace. Perhaps we need to use the word 'miracle' sparingly, because by definition miracles do not happen frequently. If they did, they would cease to be 'wondrous'.

But the fact remains that some people's illnesses do respond to prayer for healing, and that some rapid and complete recoveries have no rational explanation. There is a mystery about all healing, but especially healing in response to prayer. We cannot control it or produce it on demand, but the more we pray the more often it seems to happen.

ANOTHER VIEW

Another way of seeing the miraculous is that it is God's way of opening up our minds to the possibilities - that we do not need to be as bound and restricted as we often assume. This is meant to encourage us to live 'victoriously', refusing to accept the apparently impossible and calling on God's help if necessary.

In Bible times, sickness was one of the great 'impossibles', and through miraculous healing God gave us a vision for healthy life. It is this vision which has driven much of modern medical science and seen such success. It is rather backward-looking now to be asking God for miracles to achieve what we can now do for ourselves.

On this view, what kinds of things should we be praying for, in terms of the miraculous, today?

THE QUESTION OF DEMONS

The Bible testifies to a real struggle between godly people and the spiritual forces of evil. The creation stories in Genesis 1–3 remind us that the forces of evil were around before human beings chose to disobey their Creator. So humanity did not invent evil – although we have a special responsibility for the presence of evil on planet Earth. This makes good sense of what we see around us all the time: the fact that bad consequences seem to happen at random, regardless of individual wrongdoing. The problem of evil is bigger than ourselves.

> *Our struggle is not against flesh and blood, but against the powers of this dark world and the spiritual forces of evil.*
> **Ephesians 6:12**

This perspective is borne out in the New Testament. The ministry of Jesus sometimes involved confronting 'evil spirits' and stripping them of their power. And Paul reminds us that the Christian struggle against sin and evil is not confined to what we see here on earth.

The church has tended to emphasise individual sins and their consequences, and the need to repent of them to find healing and release. If we are going to minister to those who are ill and suffering, it is important that we understand evil in all its breadth, and respond to different situations appropriately.

SOCIAL EVIL

Sins are not just committed by individuals. Sin can become institutional and affect whole groups of people, even whole societies. Ideologies like fascism and apartheid have had enormous power over people, even over those people who 'lead' or give rise to them. There is a momentum to them that seems to be truly demonic. Individuals are caught up in something much bigger than themselves, and become instruments of pursuing it – often to their own destruction.

Similar things happen within more democratic political structures. Hundreds were allowed to die in the Irish potato famine, because of a driving political belief in *laissez faire* economics.

Sin also affects whole families. The cycle of abuse takes on a power of its own, and damages one generation after another, each one as much sinned against as sinning.

When we minister to those who are caught up in such cycles of evil, as instruments or victims or both, we must address the whole situation and not just the individual.

SPIRITUAL OPPRESSION

Everyone is tempted, and mostly these temptations come from within us (see James 1:14, Mark 7:14-23). But sometimes we have a sense of evil outside us and confronting us, of having temptations presented to us from the outside. We sense that we are being assaulted and oppressed by the forces of evil.

This seems to happen at points of personal and physical weakness. Jesus was specifically tempted by Satan during a time of fasting in the desert (Luke 4:1-2). We are assaulted where we are vulnerable – perhaps weakened by our own habitual sin, or by past hurts.

People who are unwell may have a similar sense of oppression. This may simply be an understandable human reaction to suffering. But in their illness they are indeed caught up in the wider consequences of evil in the world. We will do well to take the person's own sense of what is happening to them seriously, and pray with them for the spiritual and moral strength to withstand an unusual level of evil activity in and around their lives.

SPIRITUAL BONDAGE

The Greek *daimonidzomai* is wrongly translated 'demon possessed' and more accurately should be 'under demonic influence'. The classic case is a kind of bondage of the will, where the person appears to be no longer free to choose what is good – for themselves or for others.

Examples range from Judas, whose heart Satan entered (Luke 22:3, John 13:27), to Legion who was infested with malevolent spirits (Mark 5:1-10).

Deliverance is enabling people to live the Christian life free from any bondage to Satan. It involves repentance and confession in order to loosen spiritual bondages connected with sinful practices, and prayer to break the undue influence of the demonic. Such a ministry is the prerogative of every Christian leader engaged in pastoral care, and should be seen as part of the wider healing ministry of the church.

Exorcism is the act of expelling unclean spirits which have to some degree 'possessed' or taken over the will of the individual. It is a rare condition, commonly manifested by negative reactions to holy things. Such 'possession' is a spiritual condition still in evidence today. Often it is linked with previous involvement in the occult. Evidence includes strong reactions during prayer, aversion to the name of Jesus, nausea during a holy ceremony (such as Communion) and responding in a voice which does not belong to the person.

Because possession is a rare condition, dealing with it is a specialist ministry. Even then it is not an area to enter without extensive preparation. Such battles against evil are real, and if you lose, more harm is done than good.

> *There are two equal and opposite dangers that Christians must avoid when considering the issue of demonic encounter. The first is to assume that there is no such thing as demons or evil spirits, and the second is to see the work of the demonic in everything.*
> *The Screwtape Letters*, C S Lewis

SPIRITUAL AND PSYCHOLOGICAL

It is possible to confuse spiritual bondage with psychological illness, especially schizophrenia. This is further complicated by the possibility of such 'possession' co-existing with a psychological condition. But most people who identify themselves as 'possessed' are not, and referral to a psychiatrist or psychotherapist is the most appropriate action.

In psychological terms, the 'possession syndrome' is characterised by delusional thinking, hallucinations, and a sense of being controlled and acted upon by alien forces – sometimes interpreted by the sufferer as demons. Most psychiatrists who accept the reality of spiritual warfare find it difficult to distinguish between demonic symptoms and evidence of mental illness.

One approach is to try praying with the person. A sense of peace and stillness in the presence of God would point towards a psychological illness, whereas fearful or negative reactions would point towards the presence of evil.

The other approach is to try psychiatric treatment and see whether this gives the person a greater measure of control over their lives. There is increasing collaboration between medicine and the church in setting some patients free from addictions to malevolence which have not responded to clinical methods. Some such conditions respond to prayers for deliverance.

Church of England Policy

The decision to perform a service of exorcism should only be taken after all avenues of therapy and disease have been explored and the risks assessed. The exorcism is to be carried out only by those who have the Bishop's authority to do so. Counselling under supervision should be part of the process before and after ministry. This work should be done in close partnership with medical and other professionals.

The service itself should be simple and may include absolution, Holy Communion, anointing and the laying on of hands. The welfare of the subject is paramount and so the service should not be emotionally charged.

The House of Bishops, 1975

An exorcism may be performed only by a trained exorcist who holds a current licence to practice. It should normally take place in the presence of witnesses (at least one), and in the case of a woman patient one such witness ought to be a woman.

Every exorcist represents the bishop of his diocese, as being the centre of unity of the church in that diocese; hence the desirability that bishops should appoint priests to act as exorcists, and should ensure that they are adequately trained.

Bishop of Exeter's Report, 1964

DEALING WITH DEATH

The way we die has changed. In 1960 less than half of us died in hospital; by 1984 about 70% of deaths occurred in hospitals or hospices. This trend continues. Death has become increasingly institutionalised.

There are understandable social reasons for this.

- The whole of life has become more 'medicalised'. So it is only logical that the end of life should happen in a medical setting.

- The family structure has changed, with smaller families in nuclear units, often both parents working, a very mobile lifestyle, and immense pressures over bringing up teenagers. These conditions do not provide well for elderly relatives approaching death at home.

- In response there is increased provision for Nursing Homes, at least for those who can afford them. Hospitalisation is then just another step in institutionalised life.

As a result, death has become more distant from each of us. We seldom experience the actual death of a relative, and often have little to do with their care around this time. This has deepened the sense of mystery and taboo that surrounds death, especially in modern Western society.

Death is the final stage of human life. It is a natural event, even though in Christian terms it reflects the fallenness of creation. We are finite. Without the hope of resurrection, our existence is clearly going to end in death. Until we can accept our own mortality, we cannot accept death. And we will not be able to help others with theirs, or with the death of those close to them.

If I cannot face my own death it is conceivable that I cannot accept the patient's death. Each time we dare to get truly involved with our patients and reach a stage of acceptance, it will help us to come a step closer to acceptance of our finiteness. (Kubler Ross)

HELPING THE DYING

Death is a lonely road. If you come alongside someone who is dying, you may feel useless but it is important just to **be there**. You are part of the care which will help the person face their death.

By simply **listening**, you can help the person express their feelings of anger, or fear, or hopelessness – feelings they may not be able to express to those close to them, in case they upset them. You can join in the person's search for the meaning of their life, and the questions their life has left them with. You can share their emotional pain. As you do so, it is important to respect the person's values, and affirm their integrity.

You may be able to provide **reassurance**. They may be worried about how they are going to be cared for in the final stages of their life, or about how their family is going to be provided for and supported. You may be able to provide reassuring information, or support them in obtaining it. You can assure them of your own support, as a person and as a Christian. You can offer space for them to talk about spiritual things and the issue of mortality.

There are practical and personal **preparations for death**. You might offer to help with any unfinished business, with reviewing of life, or preparing the family for the loss.

Like a bird in a cage, the dying can choose to exhaust themselves, battering their wings against the bars. Or they can learn to live within the confines of the prison, and find to their surprise that they have the strength to sing.

Everyone should be afforded comfort and dignity at their death.

World Health Organisation

The WHO 'Mercy Target' is that everyone should be able to choose where they spend their last days, and should be able to expect good pain relief, physical comfort, and psychological support from professionals.

BEREAVEMENT

The experience of bereavement is normally a very difficult and painful one. People frequently experience a mass of intense, confusing and conflicting feelings. Each situation is different: for some the death comes as a relief after a long illness, for others the death raises their own fear of death or a fear of the future without the person who has died. Occasionally people remain unemotional, apparently unaffected by the death.

One way of making sense of these is through the **Grief Wheel**. Although rather over-simplified, it provides a helpful framework for understanding this powerful and complex experience.

Shock

People often feel numb, perhaps because to acknowledge all the feelings would be overwhelming. There is sometimes disbelief ('this hasn't really happened'), or thoughts of suicide (desire to join the deceased). People can become hysterical, and then experience irrational feelings of happiness. Thinking and activity can become slow and chaotic, although some people go into 'overdrive'.

Protest

The pain of loss can be directed inwards, as an all-pervading sense of sadness, or outwards, as anger or rage – at the deceased for dying, at others who may be blamed for the loss. People often feel guilty, if not for the death, for words spoken or not spoken, actions done or not done – 'if only…'. There may be an inner subconscious reluctance to come to terms with the death of the person – yearning after their presence, a sense of hearing, smelling or feeling them, mistaking others for them. Some people may become preoccupied with memories of the deceased, with dreams and nightmares, even with thoughts on how to recover the person.

Disorganisation

Life seems to fall apart and become confusing. People lack motivation and purpose, and lose interest in life, indifferent to things that used to animate them. They find it hard to settle to any activity. They may suffer a loss of faith ('How can God do this?') and a sense of hopelessness ('What future is there for me now?'). Some become suicidal. Many suffer a loss of confidence, and their essential sense of self-esteem is threatened – as if they are worth less, or less able, without the deceased. Anguish, anxiety, feelings of depression, and loneliness are all common, although people sometimes describe themselves as feeling 'better' as they recover from more intense depression. Concentration and memory are poor, and people become more susceptible to illnesses.

Reorganisation

As the person begins to rebuild their life, their memories of the deceased become more balanced – they can recall the good and the bad. Although the memories are still painful, they can enjoy them and are more in control of the process. The basic functioning of life gets back to normal. But with this comes changed values and a new sense of purpose in life, a different view of the relative importance of things.

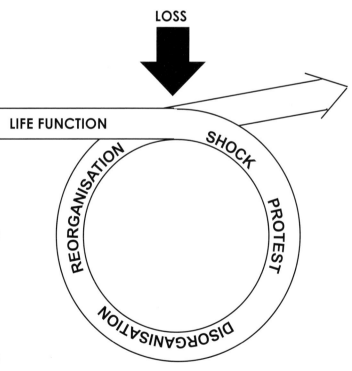

TERMS

Bereavement: the objective situation of having lost someone significant.

Grief: the emotional response to this loss.

Mourning: the actions and manner of expressing this grief, always culturally related.

LOSING – AND WINNING

The Grief Wheel can be applied to any loss – death, divorce, retirement, the loss of a limb, the general loss of good health (see box). People need to go through the four phases of the Wheel in order to come to terms with the loss, although people vary enormously in the time frame that is needed for this. Each phase merges into the next, with some movement backwards and forwards.

OTHER LOSSES

Physical
ageing
loss of hair
loss of beauty
incontinence
loss of a limb
loss of sight
loss of hearing

Family
marriage
miscarriage
cot death
having children
adopting children
having a handicapped child
death of a pet
children becoming independent
children leaving home
divorce/separation

Personal
loss of face
loss of security
loss of faith
loss of virginity
being raped
abortion
loss of innocence

Social
unemployment
retirement
loss of income
loss of credit
theft
moving house
changing jobs
moving schools

THE TASKS OF GRIEVING

The process of grieving is often described as hard work. There are certain 'tasks' to do, and the successful achievement of these tasks can lead to growth and greater psychological strength.

Task 1. To accept the loss
The loss has to be recognised, both intellectually and emotionally. The intellectual tends to come first. The emotional acceptance normally comes quite quickly afterwards, being worked through alongside the next tasks.

Task 2. To feel the pain
The person needs to 'allow' themselves to feel the pain of the loss. This can be frightening, and generally involves a bewildering confusion of difficult emotions. These need to be recognised and accepted, and to be experienced fully, not pushed down so that they do not really impinge on the person. It can be helpful to have others reassure them that their expression of these difficult emotions is OK.

Task 3: To adjust
When a loss occurs, some kind of change is inevitable. The nature and degree of this change will vary, but the task is to accept the necessary changes and to find appropriate ways of adjusting to them.

Task 4: To let go
This is the hard task of saying goodbye, or releasing the lost person or object and the emotional ties with them. This means that life, activity, relationships and interests can go on again. It is not necessary to forget, or to stop loving, but to let go and move on.

COMPLICATIONS

'Mini Wheels' can be triggered by anniversaries or other reminders of the loss. The person may feel they have gone back a stage or two, and experience earlier feelings again. But in fact Mini Wheels are usually worked through more quickly and easily, and then progress is resumed.

But major difficulties arise when people try to short-cut the stages of the Wheel, especially to avoid the painful stages of protest and disorganisation. Short-cuts do not result in successful reorganisation in the

MORE DIFFICULT

There are a number of factors which may make the process of a bereavement more difficult:

- a sudden death
- an untimely death
- an unnatural or violent death
- uncertainty over whether the death has occurred
- an unmentionable death
- a preventable death
- multiple deaths
- a death accompanied by other losses

Grieving is also more difficult with a very close relationship, especially a dependent one. And it is also more complicated with an ambivalent relationship.

Difficulties also arise from a low 'psychological strength' in the bereaved, their general health, the presence of other stresses, and the absence of social support, especially the presence of a close confidante. Some gender stereotypes also complicate the process, as do cultural values.

long term, because ignored or unresolved feelings can be triggered again by future events – and are then much harder to deal with.

FINISHING HIGHER

The Wheel is shown as finishing at a higher level than where it began, because many people grow and become stronger through the process of adjusting to a loss. This may be very difficult for the person to believe or imagine, and their highest hope might be for things to return to 'normal'. But most of those who fulfil the tasks of grieving report significant personal growth as a result.

This insight may be of special help to those whose loss of someone close to them will indeed bring them a new quality of life.

- The woman whose husband of a lifetime has constantly impeded her own freedom and development may feel guilty about entering enthusiastically into a new phase of her existence.

- The parents whose autistic child and her needs have governed life for them and their other children for many years may find it hard to channel their energies into living a more 'normal' and enterprising family life.

But it is true of all those who face painful experiences and work through them. There is hope, because better things lie beyond.

We can use the analogy of the nutcracker. Unforeseen calamities apply force that can break through the hard outer shell of personal security. The act of breaking will cause pain but it need not destroy. On the contrary, in the right environment the 'breakdown' can lead to creative growth. When old routines and behaviour patterns no longer work, the person is exposed and vulnerable (like the nut) – and is suddenly able to adopt new patterns. They can be helped to see that their hardship can open up potential for growth and development. The Christian perspective emphasises hope and purpose in the face of apparently meaningless pain and suffering.

> **Every gain is a bondage. Every loss is a freedom.**

@iStockphoto.com/Cat London

TEN TIPS AFTER A DEATH

1 Be there. *Just* be there; don't offer solutions.

2 Listen. Be accepting of the different thoughts and emotions that are expressed.

3 Show you are listening. Be clearly attentive, use simple language and touch, and show you understand something of what they are going through.

4 Encourage talk of the deceased. Mention them by name, ask about them.

5 Allow silences. They are useful thinking times, without leaving the person alone.

6 Know your own fears. Become familiar with your own difficult feelings about loss, so that they don't get mixed up with theirs.

7 Offer reassurance. What they are feeling is normal. It will take time, but there is a future.

8 Don't take anger personally. It is part of the grief. It is not directed at you.

9 Be aware of how you are affected. Your feelings of helplessness, hopelessness, frustration or anger may actually be what the other person is feeling.

10 Accept that you can't make them feel better. But even so, you are still doing something useful by being there. (Back to point 1)

YOUR LOSSES

Try to make some notes on:

My first loss
Write about the first loss you can remember. What were your feelings at the time? And how did you cope with them?

My worst loss
Then write about your most difficult loss in life so far. Again, what were your feelings and how did you cope with them?

Then reflect on:
- what is your primary way of coping with loss?
- how do you know when your grief is resolved?

This will help you understand both the process of grief itself and your own ways of handling it.

ALTERNATIVES - OLD AND NEW

Conventional Western medicine is founded on modern scientific knowledge and techniques. Despite its origins in ancient Greek pantheism and the Hypocratic Oath, modern medical practice stands or falls on scientific research and verification.

But, during the 20th century and since, there has been a gradual absorption of other approaches – to some degree a recognition of the limitations of Western medicine. Since the 1960s in particular the trend in medical thinking has been towards acknowledging the link between body, mind and spirit.

Alternative and complementary therapies are now an established part of national health care provision, and increasingly are provided on the NHS. It is estimated that some 4-5 million people in the UK have used these therapies in search of health and healing. 40% of GP partnerships provide access to them and 75% of the British public support this access. The Institute for Complementary Medicine lists nearly 80 of the main disciplines.

A MOVEMENT OF THE SPIRIT

This interest mirrors the rise of the New Age movement, with its *smorgasbord* of spiritualities, environmental issues and alternative lifestyles. This has questioned the conventional spiritualities of the established churches and offered a range of alternatives. The 'shop window' for this movement has been the Mind, Body and Spirit fairs, although these are arguably a shallow popularising of much more serious issues. In common with alternative therapies, the New Age movement has promoted self-improvement, fulfilment, and a return to 'natural' means for achieving these things.

Both alternative therapies and the New Age are counter-cultural forces, rejecting many of the values of the modern scientific world-view. Both appeal strongly to people who have believed in that world-view and found it wanting; people who once believed that truth lies in science and the material world, but discovered that those beliefs have not brought them happiness or inner health. Nor have the churches brought them a sense of the power or the presence of God. Alternative therapies have offered them self-realisation, personal equilibrium and a sense of harmony.

Some therapies maintain that our neglect of the core 'image' or 'spirit' of a person is the main reason for many chronic illnesses. The route to transformation from illness to wholeness lies in being attentive to this spirit or inner self, and linking it with larger cosmic forces. Others see health and emotional problems as a result of an imbalance or depletion of the body's energy; the aim of the therapy is to restore that energy balance.

Informed Christians can be found passionately for and vehemently against particular alternative therapies. Certainly the links between some therapies and particular religious or spiritual practices means that we must approach each with some care. But most of the therapies aim to treat the whole person – body, mind and spirit – and so have much in common with a Christian view of health which seeks to include the spiritual in the overall picture of health care.

EXTERNAL

Some therapies work on the outside of the body. These include:

- acupuncture
- aromatherapy
- reflexology
- massage
- osteopathy
- chiropractic
- Shiatsu
- Reiki

Although they are 'physical' in their application, most have a philosophy which assumes the existence of various paranormal forces. Acupuncture assumes the existence of channels or 'meridians' around the body, which can be blocked or cleared; these do not respond to any physical reality in the body (such as veins or nerves). Chiropractic believes in an 'innate intelligence' in the nervous system, which is sometimes blocked by a misalignment of the vertebral column.

However, most are inherently relaxing, and the provision of physical touch can be therapeutic, especially for those who are stressed. Touch often conveys an identification with the patient and gives them a sense of not being alone in their struggle. They can also be less intimidating to the patient than conventional medicine, and appear safer and more wholesome. But for survivors of physical abuse, touch may convey anything but care.

INTERNAL

Other therapies work on the inside of the body. These include:

- homoeopathy
- herbal remedies
- traditional Chinese medicine
- Bach flower therapies

Although they work with natural products, rather than with synthetic and chemical drugs, there is often no clear or demonstrable link between the natural substance and the improvement in health. This is particularly true of homeopathy, where the original substance (or 'tincture') is diluted so much that it cannot be detected by any scientific means. There is also increasing concern about the safety of some herbal medicines; 'natural' does not always means 'safe', and some combinations of herbs have proved fatal to some ill people.

However, there is doubtless much wisdom behind many herbal remedies, and the best practitioners open their practices to external scrutiny and verification. Also, many people worry about taking modern drugs, with their many side-effects, and natural compounds and herbs appeal more. This confidence or 'faith' in the remedy is an important component in the return to health. Placebo drugs ('dummy'

medication with no active ingredients) give an improvement in health to 30%–40% of patients. Perhaps it is more than coincidence that about the same proportion show excellent results with homeopathy, herbal remedies and other similar treatments. Provided the substances are safe, herbal and other remedies can bring people greater health and well-being – which is to be welcomed.

PSYCHIC

Then there are therapies that work on the mind or psyche of the person. These include:

- hypnotherapy
- astral projection
- meditation, especially Yoga
- Ta'i Ch'i

These therapies explicitly approach the health of the person through their inner state. They are therefore most affected by the philosophy and the spiritual orientation of their origins. Anyone accessing this kind of remedy is likely to have to put their 'faith' in it in quite an explicit way. From a Christian point of view, they need to be approached with caution.

However, many such therapies bring a greater sense of self-worth and purpose in life, and encourage a belief in the spiritual. They can help some people resolve some of their inner conflicts, which is part of God's will for them. But it must be said that few people progress from such practices to embracing any kind of Christian faith.

FURTHER INFORMATION

Further information on many of these therapies, with points for and against them from a Christian point of view, can be found on the internet at www.eauk. org/handlewithcare. Some of the material on these pages is drawn from that website.

Complementary and Alternative Medicine, by Dr Robina Coker, Christian Medical Fellowship 2008,

Alternative Medicine: The Christian Handbook, by Donal P O'Mathuna, Walt Larimore, Zondervan 2006.

Examining Alternative Medicine by Paul Reisser and Dale Nabe, IVP 2001

WEIGHING THEM UP

What these new therapies have in common is that they encourage patients to reconsider their lifestyle and their basic orientation in life, encouraging better self-regard and a sense of harmony. Such a holistic re-evaluation of life cannot be carried out without reference to the spiritual. Although these therapies focus on health care, they invariably invoke some form of 'spirituality'. Some of this will be at variance with Christian perspectives.

But the inclusion of the spiritual is in keeping with a Christian perspective on healing, and far from being a threat, they offer the church both an opportunity and a challenge. The opportunity is the climate of renewed interest in the spiritual in the search for health and healing. The challenge is to lead people on from a spiritual awakening to spiritual discernment, and help them to 'test the spirits' rather than embrace anything that seems to work (1 Thessalonians 5:19-22).

The 'spiritual' element varies greatly from one practitioner to another. It is good to encourage people to ask a practitioner about their spiritual values and how these link into the therapy as they practice it.

Need for time

With large patient case-loads, most doctors are simply too busy to listen to how the patient is as a whole person and to explore some of the connected issues. The average GP spends six minutes with each patient.

Many complementary therapists will take at least an hour for a client's initial visit, and will take a full case history. This allows the patient to talk about all the various things that are troubling them. Being given time is frequently mentioned as important by those who have found complementary therapies helpful.

To be listened to is to be valued and respected – something which can be missed in a more clinical climate where the patient can feel excluded from their own therapeutic journey.

Need for self-worth

If someone senses a need for greater meaning or purpose in their life, they may become interested in approaches to healing that emphasise self-satisfaction and fulfilment. Therapies such as aromatherapy and massage are often undertaken as a 'treat' or even as a consolation in time of difficulty or depression. People are encouraged to be kind to themselves, and to harness the spiritual resources and powers which are locked up within their bodies and which are ignored in conventional medicine. The body becomes a sensual medium for pleasurable activities which promote one's sense of self-worth.

This kind of therapy fosters a sense of partnership in the healing journey between patient and therapist, which affirms the person's worth and importance. But our society's preoccupation with the beautiful and healthy lifestyle, when taken to excess, can make people disillusioned with their bodies. Such a philosophy seldom has room for the valuing of the disabled and the infirm.

Need for regulation

Apart from chiropractic and osteopathy, anyone can practice complementary therapies without any qualifications. There is widespread concern amongst the mainstream medical professions about the lack of centralised and accountable bodies for regulating the wide range of therapies available.

Linked to this is the need for recognised training and qualifications, and the need for continuing research to scrutinise the outcomes of these therapies and establish which are genuinely helpful and in which conditions.

Regulation is a standard part of all reputable health care. It improves practice and assures good patient care. Until such regulations are in place for alternative therapies, it is important for the patient to check the qualifications of their therapist and to satisfy themselves that this is a person to be trusted.

For a critical appraisal of complementary therapies from a Christian perspective, contact:

Mr Doug Harris
Reachout Trust
24 Ormond Road
Richmond, Surrey
TW10 6TH
0845 241 2158
rt@reachouttrust.org

For a positive appraisal of these therapies, again from a Christian perspective, contact:

Revd John Huggett
Breath Ministries
Weald House
10a High Street
Tunbridge Wells, Kent TN1 1UX
01892 512520
ciphuggett@yahoo.co.uk

SKILLED HELPERS

PURPOSE

This Unit outlines some of the main human skills and personal attitudes that are needed by all those who engage with ill people, whether in the church or in the medical setting.

CONTENTS

The importance of being   38
Self awareness   40
Able to listen?   42
Emotional skills   44
Conceptual skills   46
Interpersonal skills   48
Weigh yourself   50

THE IMPORTANCE OF BEING

In today's culture, we are conditioned to believe that achievement, productivity and success are all-important. There is a relentless drive towards efficiency, cost-effectiveness and optimum functioning – of machines, of institutions, of individuals. Everything needs to be quantifiable, registered and recorded. The emphasis is on activity and performance.

As Christians we talk about being saved by grace and not by works. But then we engage in a life of unremitting activity, often with a disdain for quietness, reflection and 'being'. As a result we live life on a rather superficial level, not really engaging with others, and escaping even from ourselves. Thus we thwart any significant development of character and maturity. We have lost the divine insight that 'I am what I am' (Exodus 3:14).

YOU ARE WHAT YOU DO?

What message does such a society give about human values? In particular, what is it saying about the elderly, the disabled, the damaged, the unemployed, the retired? The implication is that the less active, the less productive, are less important. Activity is declared to be good and admirable in itself.

In retirement, many elderly people feel obliged to present themselves as 'busier than ever', lest they are perceived as worthless, having no clear function or role in society. People congratulate them for being 'sprightly for their years', again valuing their activity while making allowance for their aging bodies. As age takes its toll, people are aware of their dependence on medical and social support, in order to keep active and live the 'good life'.

It is a message also picked up, unconsciously, by those who fall ill. A person who has been ordering their own affairs, progressing various plans and projects, creating their own future and destiny, suddenly finds themselves dependent on others, helpless and vulnerable. If they see a doctor or enter the hospital environment, they become a 'patient' – someone who is passive, someone who is treated.

THE GIFT OF HELPLESSNESS

Such attitudes are even more stark in our dealings with those who cope with a severe disability. But despite their inactivity and dependence (or perhaps because of it), the person who can do nothing for themselves often becomes the pivot on which the happiness of many others turns.

Parents sometimes speak of the blessing or enrichment that a severely disabled child has brought to them. The power of helplessness can evoke love which may enrich the whole texture of relationships within a family.

The presence of such a disabled person can make a profound difference, and cause people to focus not on things done – activity, function, productivity – but on the feelings and moods of the people involved. In the midst of the stress, anger and pressures of coping with a difficult situation, people become concerned with the quality of life.

CREATED TO BE

Scripture teaches that we are made in the image of God. It is this – rather than our activity – which gives us our unique status within creation, and makes us of unique worth.

In Christian faith the emphasis is on the relationship we can have with God through Jesus Christ. It is a relationship of grace, where we are the recipients of all God has done. Salvation is essentially receptive and passive, and this is an important grounding for our understanding of the nature of the Christian life. That life comprises two aspects: activity and being – and our basic worth as human beings resides in our being rather than in our doing.

- **God created us as human persons**, not as robots or machines. The development of our character is of ultimate worth, and affects all that we do. It is 'who we are' that will go with us beyond death into eternity. Excessive activity depletes our personal resources, and sometimes causes stress and burnout.

- **Life is about relationships** – with God and with others. Modern society is fragmented, and many of us do not really know how to cope with relationships. The phenomenal rise of 'counselling' is a symptom of this. The development of the skills of relationship need to be nurtured.

- **'Being' provides us with a deepening spirituality**. Christian life finds its highest expression in worship. Sadly, patterns of worship often reinforce our activist tendency, with a clear pattern of things to say and do, and little opportunity for us just to be the people of God. It is from this 'being with God' that all life is meant to proceed.

DEVELOPING OUR BEING

The rest of this chapter deals with aspects of our 'being' which are important for all those who relate to people who are ill. They are equally important in the church setting in praying for healing, and in the hospital setting in promoting the health of the whole person alongside modern medical care. Without this development of 'who we are', our ministry will always be shallow.

EXERCISE

Imagine you have been praying for the healing of a person in your church, or have been visiting them in hospital or in their home, and their condition remains unchanged. As you think about praying for them or visiting them again, note down:

- *what personal strengths you feel you can bring to this person*

- *what challenges you most about this circumstance*

- *what weaknesses you discover about yourself as you consider how to pray or what to say and do*

SELF AWARENESS

Whether we realise it or not, most of what people perceive of us comes not from what we say or do, but from who we are. The 'communication cake' shows what a small percentage of what people 'hear' is in the words themselves. Most of what they hear us say is 'tonal' (how we say it) and 'non-verbal' (body language, etc.).

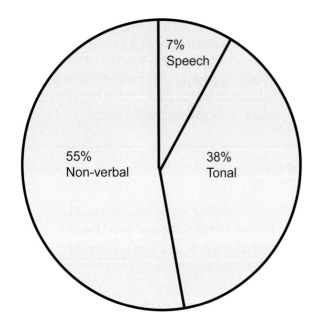

7%
Speech

55%
Non-verbal

38%
Tonal

WHO AM I?

We are all different. Each of us has a unique personality, with various gifts and abilities. We approach others and relate to them in very different ways. This can be channelled to make us more effective helpers.

But how well do we know ourselves? Try to write your 'autobiography' using these headings:

- My goals and priorities in life
- Past influences on me
- My strengths and weaknesses
- How I compensate for my weaknesses
- What drives and dominates my thoughts
- How I respond to criticism and direction
- How I say I care

Or simply write a list of adjectives or characteristics which describe you:

- physical features: short, good looking, big nose...

- personality: friendly, impatient, independent...

- religious beliefs: traditional, prone to doubt, on fire...

- moral values: opposed to euthanasia, pro-gay...

- social roles: committed parent, reluctant daughter...

Then look over what you have written. Use two colours of highlighter: one on things that you feel are desirable about yourself, the other on things that aren't. This will begin to reveal your self-image.

What does it say about yours?

Many Christians have a poor self-image. We know we are sinners, and certainly pride is one of the greatest of sins. This often stops us from developing a positive image of ourselves – as people who, despite our faults, are made in God's image and have many good characteristics. This 'image' comes over to other people, in how we talk and how we live our lives. Paul had a more balanced self-image. When in prison and facing the likelihood of death, he wrote:

I have learned to be content, in whatever circumstances. I know what it is to be in need, and I know what it is to have plenty. I have learned the secret of being content in any situation, whether well-fed or hungry, whether living in plenty or in want.

It will be hard for other people to believe God wants the best for them, when 'who you are' shows you don't believe He wants to give the best to you.

How far are you 'content' with yourself and your circumstances?

YOUR FAMILY CREST

Draw a larger version of the crest below. Fill in the four quarters. In words or pictures indicate the qualities you think you have:

- inherited from your father
- inherited from your mother
- gained from your childhood
- gained from your adolescence

Along the bottom scroll, write your motto – a short saying that sums up your outlook on life now.

THE SPIRITUAL

How would you describe your spiritual life at the moment? Tick the two closest:

- ☐ slipping
- ☐ growing
- ☐ up and down
- ☐ on the injured list

- ☐ OK but…
- ☐ on half-time working
- ☐ lazy
- ☐ stormy

- ☐ moonlight and roses
- ☐ stuck
- ☐ better than yesterday

Knowing Yourself

Circle a number on these three scales, to indicate where you rate yourself:

Self Put-Down
God blundered when He made me. I will never be any good.

-5 -4 -3 -2 -1 0 1 2 3 4 5

Self Esteem
God doesn't make mistakes. I am a valuable person because He made me.

Self Pity
I'm not clever, good-looking or good at anything. Nobody really loves me.

-5 -4 -3 -2 -1 0 1 2 3 4 5

Self Acceptance
Whatever my weaknesses, I am a whole person. God has given me all I need to live life.

Self Defeat
There is no point in trying, because I know I'll fail. I'll never make it.

-5 -4 -3 -2 -1 0 1 2 3 4 5

Self Confidence
I can do anything God wants me to do. Failure only makes me try harder.

Then consider your self-image 12 months ago. Put a square round a number on each of the three scales. Then draw an arrow to indicate any movement. Which way are you travelling? Have you moved any great distance?

ABLE TO LISTEN?

Before we say anything to a patient in hospital, or offer a prayer for healing in church, we need to listen to the person who is unwell. We need to listen to the whole person, the unique person who is not just another case of this or that. If we don't know how to listen, we will not know how to treat each person as an individual, as Jesus did.

Reflect on a time when you felt you were carefully listened to. How did it make you feel?

Then reflect on a time when you were not really listened to, when the other person did not 'hear' what you were saying. How did *that* make you feel?

There is therapeutic, healing value in being listened to. It makes people more whole, and opens them up to more of the healing touch of God.

WHAT ARE WE LISTENING *TO*?

Words

This may sound obvious, but the words and phrases people use will often say more than they themselves realise. This is particularly true when they are struggling to put things into words.

Inner Conflict: The person is trying to come to terms with what seem impossible choices.
  'I suppose I ought to…'
  'I keep telling myself…'
  'I can't convince myself…'

Avoidance: The person is not coping with difficult feelings, so they talk in general or intellectual terms, or escape questions through forgetting.
  'People get upset when…'
  'I can't remember…'
  'I think…'

Poor self-image: The person's positive self-image is suffering, or their low self-image is having a field day.
  'I am just a housewife…'
  'I am only 5' 6" tall…'
  'It doesn't matter about me…'

You can gently pick up these kinds of phrases, and ask people how they feel about that. This may help the underlying feelings to become explicit. Any picture language the person uses can be helpful in this:
  'I'd give my right hand for…'
  'I feel bogged down by…'
  'There's a lead ball in my stomach...'

Allowing a person to 'hear' their own language may enable them to become aware of the depth and intensity of their feelings.

Tone

A depressed person will often sound monotonous – even to the extent of producing yawning and tiredness in the listener! An anxious person may sound high-pitched, and talk very rapidly and jumpily.

So listen to the tone, pitch and speed of what people say.

Silences
There are different kinds of silences, and they mean different things.
- the silence of despair
- the sullen silence, refusing to speak
- the reflective, thoughtful silence
- the stunned silence, where there are simply no words for what has happened to them
- the mid-sentence silence, groping for the right word for an unfamiliar experience
- the silence that is choking back tears
- the retreat into oneself

As listeners, we need to learn to interpret the silence. We also need to respect it, and not feel the need to dash in with words.

Thought
Behind the person's words will be their assumptions – ways of thinking about themselves and the world. Where these are distortions of reality, they are likely to hinder the healing process. These may be cultural values, family expectations, religious viewpoints, simplistic understandings of life.

Reflecting back these thoughts to the person may help them to discover any discrepancies and distortions for themselves.

Emotions
Tears are an alternative language. Rather than waiting for the crying to stop, it is better to listen to the tears and try to discern that it is saying.

The body also has a language. Anxiety may be registered by restlessness, twisting and turning the hands or a ring on a finger. Avoidance may be shown by a person's inability to look you in the eye. Discomfort may be indicated by the way a person is sitting. Depression may be communicated by indifference to their physical appearance.

Lifestyle
Listen for clues about the rest of the person's life. Are they a loner? Do they have few friends? Are they a workaholic, with no time for the family? Do they need help with their use of money? Are they undisciplined in their diet, or their sleep pattern? All these affect the health of the whole person.

Relationships
Many relationships are hurting rather than healing. What is happening in the person's relationships? Which of them are nurturing, and which are failing? Can the person cope with intimacy, and are they avoiding it? Do they have good friendships? Is their relational life helping them get better, or pulling them down?

A LISTENING EXERCISE

Try this exercise with someone, to develop your listening skills. As well as being an exercise for you, it will also benefit the person to whom you are listening. People rarely get the opportunity to be well listened to!

- Ask the person to share with you a concern that is currently troubling them. What it is will depend on the nature of your relationship with them. It may be something for which they would value your prayers.

- Listen to them for up to seven minutes, without interruption. Do not ask questions, or make comments. Let the person speak. At most, allow yourself affirming nods and 'mm's to assure them you are paying attention!

- When they feel they have finished, ask them what they feel is the most important thing they have shared with you during those minutes. Then simply say back to them what they have said, so they can hear how it sounds. The person may want to say a little more at this point, but don't allow it to develop into conversation.

- Then ask them whether there is any action they would like to take in the light of what they have said. Again reflect back to them what they say, so they hear what they are saying.

- Finally, ask how they feel, having shared these things with you. This will help you know how they are. If you pray for them, use some of their feeling words in your prayer.

EMOTIONAL SKILLS

EMPATHY

When you draw alongside someone else and enter into how they are feeling, this is called empathy. It is a skill that most of us have to learn, as few people have it as a natural ability.

You may have a natural *sympathy* for others. You have experienced similar feelings to theirs, and by talking about those feelings, you can reassure the other person that they are not 'odd' or (worse) going mad. Sympathy says, 'I know just how you feel. I had a similar experience when…' This helps the other person know you understand their situation, but it also shifts the focus from their story to yours. What results is a more superficial conversation, or (worse) a conversation about *you*!

Empathy is different. Empathy says, 'So you're feeling pretty anxious about this, then.' It shows you have picked up the other person's feelings, seen how life looks from their point of view. It keeps the focus on *their* story, and helps them explore that story, knowing you are with them in it. A good empathetic response will pick up the other person's words, especially their feeling words, to show you have 'heard' how they feel. You do not need to have experienced something similar to what they are going through, to be able to make a genuine empathetic response.

VULNERABILITY

As you listen to someone speak about their pain and their illness, you may well find some of your own feelings are engaged. This may particularly be true if some of this person's story is similar to your own experience, or to the lives of people close to you. Their pain may 'touch' you where it hurts.

Allowing someone else's story to touch us, is called vulnerability. It is mostly a positive emotional skill, helping us understand the other person, and helping them feel 'heard'. Be prepared to weep with the other person, to be silent with them, or whatever, when their experience touches yours. We are called to be 'wounded healers' – people who can draw on our own painful experiences in bringing healing to others.

You need to keep appropriate boundaries in this, and know your own limitations. If you find your own feelings overwhelming, you will need to step back to allow your feelings to settle. You need to tell the person why you are doing this, so they don't feel it is something about *them*.

Reflect on situations of ill-health (physical or emotional) that would disturb or unsettle you. Or life situations you would find so engaging that it would be difficult to give your full concentration to the other person. Write them down below. Being aware of these will help you handle your feelings when such situations arise.

NON-POSSESSIVE WARMTH

When we engage with someone else's story, we are sometimes drawn into inappropriate responses. One of these is to take command of the person – as if we are 'mother' and they are a little child – and then to smother them with our love and care in order to take their pain away. This is sometimes because we find the sound of their pain too disturbing. Or we find it fulfilling to 'rescue' people as this gives us a sense of mission and purpose in life.

C S Lewis once described a woman in his church who was very keen to sort out other people's problems. You could tell who these people were 'by the hunted look on their faces.'

Non-possessive warmth is the ability to care genuinely for others without trying to take control of their lives or their situation. It is a difficult emotional balance – we do not want our care for others to become clinical. But our natural tendency to take undue responsibility for the situation and for the ill person must be resisted.

POWERLESSNESS

No matter how able and experienced we are, there will be times when we reach the limits of our ability to help. This is a good reminder that it is not our role to rescue the person, and that is not us who are their Saviour. In all our work with ill people, we must be willing to be powerless, confident not in ourselves but in the healing work of God in people's lives.

But it is important that we do not feel threatened by situations in which we feel useless or out of our depth. Sometimes we simply have to express our care, without any assurance of help or improvement. This may also be a time for referral to someone else who may be better skilled than us. This is not an abandoning of care – it is offering the best help available, even if it is not ourselves.

BALANCE

To be a blessing to those who are ill, we do not need to be perfect, but we need some balance if we are to help them at an unsettling time:

- taking the power and love of God seriously, but not ourselves too seriously – a sense of humour.

- having hope for good things, but not easily shocked by bad things.

- working for full recovery, but able to live with failure.

- not quick to blame themselves or others when things don't work out.

EMPATHY EXERCISE

Ask a friend to share with you a recent experience that has either been joyful or challenging for them. Listen to them for 5-10 minutes. Do not interrupt them, except perhaps to ask for clarification when you simply do not understand what they have said.

As you listen, note their 'feeling' words. When they have finished, try to summarise back to them how you think they felt in relation to this experience.

Then ask your friend if you picked up their feelings accurately. You could also ask them how it felt to hear their own 'feelings' reflected back to them.

Afterwards, consider on your own whether there were times when you were tempted to

- interrupt with your own similar experience?

- give advice?

- challenge the speaker?

You might want to consider the reasons for these responses in yourself, and talk them through with someone.

CONTROL

Look at 2 Kings 4: 25-30. Reflect on how Elijah relates to this distressed woman, and note who is in control.

CONCEPTUAL SKILLS

WORLD VIEW

Our dealings with people who are ill will be affected by the way we think. We owe people our thoughtful involvement in their lives. Care for the unwell is not all about emotions and feelings. It is about being alongside them as they struggle with the meaning of their lives. There is a place in this ministry for people with strong intellectual abilities.

Each person has their own way of viewing the world. They will have assumptions about the deepest issues of life, assumptions which they will not often articulate or even be aware of. They are part of a 'culture', a way of living life.

People do not *think* things in their world view – they *know* them. It's obvious. It's unthinkable it should be any different. It's just the way the world is – or the way *their* world is. For you, the world may seem very different.

If we have a ministry with the unwell, we (like Jesus) will meet many different kinds of people. Many will have a different world view from us, perhaps also a different culture, race, social background, sexuality, religion. It is important to be able to relate to people across the divide of culture and world view.

We need to begin by understanding our own world view – to see how we are acting out of our own particular convictions and values. We can ask for this world view to be respected, but we cannot impose it on others. We must be especially careful with others who are at a vulnerable point in their lives.

We then need to understand and respect the other person's world view. For example, we can try to ascertain:

- what is sacred to them
- what brings them joy
- what causes them fear
- where they feel 'connected' and with whom
- how they understand God or some 'Greater Power'

SUSPENDING JUDGEMENT

When people are ill and vulnerable, they will sometimes reveal things about their personal lives which normally they would keep to themselves. Their situation, beliefs or lifestyle may conflict with your values, and at this point they are particularly vulnerable to your reactions to what they say. This is not the time to pass judgement. It is the time to express acceptance of them as a person, and to leave other issues aside.

Suspending our judgement is partly an emotional skill, but it is also an intellectual one. We have particular convictions about what is right and wrong, what is acceptable and what is shocking. It is right and proper to have these convictions. But we need the intellectual humility to recognise that some of our views may be wrong. And we need the intellectual discipline not to engage in discussion of moral and personal issues in an inappropriate setting.

HOW DO I SEE THE WORLD?

Just	Unjust
Peaceful	Boring
Challenging	Frightening
Beautiful	Brutal
Amazing	Complicated
Meaningful	Meaningless
Caring	Uncaring
Created	Evolved
Purposeful	Pointless
Hopeful	Despairing

This is not the right time or place to explore different moral points of view, or express disapproval or shock about the person's life. At this point you are coming alongside them as a representative of Christ the Healer, and encouraging them to trust in Christ for the health of their whole person. Your judgement of them will only get in the way of this. It is the time simply to respect the opinions of those who are different from you.

HANDLING DOUBT

Doubt naturally arises when experience and faith seem to conflict. People sense a difference between what they believe and what is actually happening. Illness can trigger doubt that God really cares about me, or about whether God is fair, or really in control of the world, or whether He is there at all. Those who stand alongside them can also experience the same doubts.

As Christians we need to become more comfortable with doubt. Job, Thomas, Jeremiah, Elijah, Moses, are all recorded as doubting, but we read such passages very negatively. Perhaps they are included in Scripture to show us that doubt is part of the terrain over which faith sometimes has to travel.

Doubt is not unbelief, it is not the abandoning of faith. It is faith asking questions, voicing uncertainties. God does not call us to bury our uncertainties, but to persevere with them, and to hope for their resolution. In this midst of the doubts of an unwell person, we can affirm their experience and help them not to give up hope.

ENCOURAGING HOPE

Hope is the conviction that something good lies ahead. It is not merely a desire, or a natural optimism, or wishful thinking. Christian hope is based on facts, on truth, on reality.

Hope is a universal human need, essential for health and the quality of life.

> *Hope, faith and a purpose in life is medicinal. This is not merely a statement of belief but a conclusion proved by meticulously scientific experiment.*

(H G Wolf)

Hope can make a desperate situation tolerable. Hope can allow a dying person to confront reality, while giving them the strength to go on living.

When people are under stress, they are susceptible both to people who generate hope and those who generate hopelessness. Our contact with them can have a significant impact on their perception of their situation. It is important that our view of life is characterised by hope.

This hope can take various forms. It could be hope for an improvement in their physical condition, relief from pain, the ability to resume normal life. For many it will include hope beyond death, even for those with no Christian faith. It may simply be the hope to be remembered as a unique and loving individual. Some may find a new faith in God; others may regress into childhood faith, at least for a time.

> **I do not consider myself dying of cancer, but living despite it. I do not look upon each day as another day closer to death, but another day of life to be appreciated and enjoyed.**
> **Orville Kelly**

HOPE FACTORS

Nursing research in 1993 identified some factors which hinder hope, and others that foster it:

Hindering Factors
- sense of isolation or abandonment
- continuous pain or discomfort
- being treated as of little value

Fostering Factors
- ongoing supportive relationships
- light-heartedness
- determination and courage
- a sense of serenity
- some attainable aim or purpose
- spiritual beliefs and practices
- uplifting memories
- affirmation of worth and individuality

INTERPERSONAL SKILLS

GENUINENESS

Praying for others or caring for others is not a 'rescue' game where the strong help the weak. At the heart of all Christian service is a genuine relationship, however brief and professional it may be. We are to be open and sincere (2 Corinthians 2:17-18).

This genuineness is particularly important because we are dealing with people who are hurting and are in need. They may ask awkward questions, and they need and deserve the truth – at least as far as we can see it. They don't need a pious sermon full of second-hand thoughts, or our fantasies about how life is. People need to know that we are not out to patronise them or to 'do them good'.

We too are on a journey towards wholeness, and it does not help to disguise the fact. If we can be genuine about our fears, hopes and limitations, then perhaps the person we are supporting may become able to do likewise.

IMMEDIACY

Immediacy is helping people reflect more sharply on issues. It is not designed to 'corner' people, make them feel uncomfortable, or catch them out. But it aims to enable people to come to terms with parts of their situations which they are glossing over or leaving to one side.

Imagine Jim, who has just been diagnosed with cancer, says the following.

> *Everyone is upset because of the biopsy report. None of us were prepared for this. But still, that's life, they say. You have to get on and make the best of things. No use crying over spilt milk, eh? No doubt they will all miss me.*

As you listen, it is hard to avoid the thought that Jim is thinking of everyone – but himself. It may be that he is an absolute saint; it may be that he can't face looking at his own death, so talks about everyone else in order to avoid it.

Immediacy is being aware of this, and offering a response which invites the person to become aware of this too. So a response might be:

> *I am sure they will miss you. You obviously care about them very much, and how they will cope. I guess it must be hard for you too.*

Confrontation has the same goal but is more robust. It concentrates on discrepancies in thoughts, feelings and actions. A lot of trust needs to be built up before such confrontation is attempted, and generally it is not a skill that carers or visitors would appropriately use. But strong inconsistencies in what someone is saying and doing might indicate referral to a trained counsellor who may be able to help the person forward.

©iStockphoto.com/Sergey Rusakov

EMPOWERING

We need to be aware of the issue of 'power' in our relationships, wherever we find ourselves in a strong or privileged position. If we are not careful, we can abuse this power, whether we mean to or not. There is a skill in wielding power well, and it is one which needs to be learnt and fostered by all those who minister to ill people.

You may not feel very powerful – in fact, quite the opposite. But if you are visiting the sick or praying with them, you are definitely (from their point of view) the person with power and authority. Indeed, when people are feeling weak and vulnerable, they will sometimes *invite* us to exercise power over them. They may feel they are the victims of their ailment, and they may look to us to 'rescue' them, drawing on the power of God at our disposal.

Part of our task is to use our strong position to give a sense of power and control to the ill person. Many people can be rendered weak and dependent by illness. Part of their healing is to believe in it themselves, and to play their part in working towards wholeness in their life. People have response-ability for their illness, and we need to keep giving it back to them.

We may need to work against some of our own inner feelings and desires in this. Some of us can easily get 'hooked' by the 'rescue script', effectively agreeing that the ill person is a poor victim who needs to be saved from their ordeal – by us! This can do great things for our ego, but it is in the end a very negative message to the person who is ill. It is more caring to affirm their own worth in God's eyes, encourage in them a sense of faith and hope, and be willing to stand with them as they look to God for a greater measure of health. If we find this hard to do, we may need help in understanding ourselves better.

BEING NON-DIRECTIVE

Non-Directive Counselling is a form of therapy which allows the client to set the agenda and gives them the responsibility to do their own work. The counsellor merely offers open questions which allow the person to reflect more sharply on what they have been saying. This is a kind of 'mirroring' process in which the counsellor:

- summarises the content of what is said, focusing on feelings

- invites the client to pick out the issues which strike them as important

- asks the client what they would like to do in the light of insights gained.

The counsellor is careful not to give advice, or to intrude on the client's story. It assumes that insight will be gained by the client themselves as to why their problem has occurred, and that the client will change their behaviour accordingly.

There is much wisdom here for Christians who visit or pray with the sick. Such an approach gives the person a key role in their own healing. It is a good counter-balance to the 'passive' role generally expected both by the modern medical establishment and by many healing services where the role of the 'healer' is prominent. It is especially important in emotionally-charged healing services, where people can be extremely open to the suggestions of other – too much so for their own good.

TEAMWORK

Traditionally, the pattern of most Christian ministry has been very individualistic. This has been particularly true of the ordained ministry, where a key ability has been that of shouldering pastoral responsibility alone. Unconsciously perhaps, many of us have assumed that this is how ministry should be done, and ministry today continues to attract people with high 'go it alone' abilities.

But the care of the sick needs to be done by people with good teamwork abilities. No-one can be the expert on all aspects of life. If we are to help people to become well in the whole of their life, this will involve medicine, relationships, life-style, environment, spirituality, society and so on. We will only have one part to play in that, and must work with others to foster the person's overall health. Indeed, we must learn to trust the judgement of others, especially where it seems to cut across our own individual certainties. That combined wisdom will be more 'true' than any single perspective.

NOTES

WEIGH YOURSELF

Charles Harris once referred to 'people who feel a special sympathy with the sick, and for that reason have experienced a vocation to minister to them'. It would be good for you to weigh up whether you have a 'vocation' to serve the needs of ill people. Part of that will be a sense of sympathy for people in this kind of need – doing it for other reasons is a dangerous business. But part of it will also be weighing up whether you have the right abilities and attitudes; and then being willing to develop the ones which are somewhat weak in yourself at present.

So go back over the pages of this Unit and reflect on the various abilities and skills referred to. What are your strengths and weaknesses in each? (Talk this over with a good friend to try to make sure you are not fooling yourself!) Then decide which areas of yourself need to be developed if you are going to serve ill people well in the name of Christ.

Able to 'be'

Emotional skills

Self-awareness

Conceptual skills

Able to listen

Interpersonal skills

VISITING THE SICK

PURPOSE

This Unit describes what is involved in being a chaplaincy 'Visitor' in a modern hospital. It is a key unit for those who will fulfil this role, but any who find themselves in the hospital context will find much useful information here.

CONTENTS

The modern NHS context   52
The nature of chaplaincy   54
Body and spirit   56
Being a visitor   58
A word about wards   60
Knowing what to say   62
Good visiting practice   64
On confidentiality   66
Is it for me?   68

THE MODERN NHS CONTEXT

©iStockphoto.com/mustafa deliormanli

A CULTURE OF CHANGE

Life in Britain's hospitals never stays still. As each one expands and evolves, they often appear to be continuous building sites as another wing is planned and constructed.

Life within the buildings is also continuously changing, often with dramatic speed. This is sometimes to do with clinical decisions about what is strategic or effective care; but in the last few decades a lot of change has been caused by Government. Although the Tory 'internal market' for health care was abolished by Labour, hospitals are still managed by NHS Trusts. These Trusts are under constant political pressure to treat more patients and to reduce waiting lists.

A CULTURE OF MANAGEMENT

Part of that change has been the introduction of the culture of management. NHS Trusts now operate a kind of 'business', and some Trusts have merged into 'superTrusts' – some the size of multi-national companies. Greater professionalism and accountability has been introduced into the way a hospital functions, often against a prevailing culture of vocation and care.

IN AND OUT

25 years ago, most patients who were seriously ill would spend several weeks in hospital. Today the average stay in hospital is four days; even triple by-pass patients can expect to be discharged in seven.

Reflect for a few minutes on what difference this makes to the work of the hospital chaplaincy.

This has resulted in a situation where

- clinical staff are under pressure to produce 'value for money'
- medicine as a 'vocation' rather than a job is under threat
- patients are seen as 'consumers'
- resources are stretched because the demands on them.

A PLACE FOR CHAPLAINCY?

There was a time when the work of the hospital chaplaincy was autonomous. From the Health Act of 1948 until the Tory reforms of the early 1990s, hospital chaplains did whatever they thought was right for patients, and few would question it. Early diagrams of hospital administration structures showed the chaplain only a short distance away from the Chief Nurse or Matron, and held in the same esteem. Chaplains would not expect anyone to oversee or question their work. Overall, there was an emphasis on religious observances within the hospital context, and the upkeep of chapels – undeniably the prerogative of ordained clergy.

In 1991 there was some fear about whether the new Trusts would retain a commitment to chaplains. In fact there are now more chaplains than ever before; in bigger hospitals there are whole teams of them. But chaplaincy now comes under the hospital's organisational structures.

- The hospital chaplain today has a **line manager**. The chaplain's work will be appraised and they will be set objectives to fulfil. Their performance will be monitored. A senior chaplain may manage other chaplains; most chaplains will manage a team of volunteer visitors, and be responsible for their work. There are clear lines of accountability.
- The chaplain is now a member of an **interdisciplinary team** – not someone who is simply a religious functionary. Their work is not done in isolation but as part of a team effort with all other hospital staff. Between them this team is able to provide care at the different

'levels' of human existence – physical, psychological and spiritual.

These reforms of the structures of care have been challenging to implement, both for medical and for chaplaincy staff. But overall, health care chaplaincy has prospered as a result. Its place within the wider structures of the hospital has given chaplaincy a platform from which to promote spiritual values. By and large the NHS has welcomed a renewed emphasis on the spiritual dimension to patient care, and many chaplains provide education on spiritual, pastoral and ethical issues for hospital staff.

A World Health Organisation report once claimed that the single most important factor for health in a hospital is the atmosphere – the 'spirit' in which medicine is practised. Chaplaincy plays a key role in promoting the nurturing atmosphere that encourages a return to the full health and strength of the whole person.

BEING ILL

Think for a few minutes about what it is like to be ill. Recall a time when you were ill. This will help you stay 'tuned' to the people you visit.

How did you feel - physically and emotionally?

How were your relatives affected?

What was the most helpful thing done for you or said to you?

What was the most _unhelpful_ thing?

COME FROM AFAR

With the closure of smaller hospitals and the emerging of large regional hospitals which can offer specialised care, more people are going into hospital further from home.

Reflect for a few minutes on what difference this makes to the place of personal and spiritual care for patients.

THE NATURE OF CHAPLAINCY

When the NHS was established in 1948, hospital authorities were advised that they should 'provide for the spiritual needs of both patients and staff'. Bigger hospitals had to provide a chapel, and shifts had to be such as allowed staff to attend services of worship. Hospitals were obliged to appoint chaplains, in consultation with church authorities – full-time posts for hospitals of 750 patients or more.

The last central guidelines on hospital chaplaincy were issues by the NHS Executive in 1992. These built on the 'patient's charter', establishing a duty to respect patients' religious and cultural beliefs. The guidelines lay down that each hospital should 'make every effort to provide for the spiritual needs of patients and staff', while recognising the welfare needs of both Christians and non-Christians.

In recent years the significant role and workload of the chaplain has increasingly been recognised, and the number of full-time posts has risen, from 108 in 1976 to 400 in 1999. Today there are also 1300 part-time chaplains.

THE NEED FOR CHAPLAINCY

The modern chaplaincy provides a 'service' like any other department in the hospital, producing objectives, formulating business plans and participating in appraisals.

SURVEY

In a survey in Leeds:

- 24% of patients had talked to a chaplain or visitor during that hospital visit
- 86% would not be offended if a chaplain spoke to them if not asked
- 48% saw the chaplaincy as part of the 'team' on their ward
- 75% thought that the role of chaplains included helping patients deal with fear and anxiety resulting from illness

---

- Serious illness can cause people to question familiar values and beliefs. They often struggle to find **meaning** in their pain and distress. Spiritual care offers patients the possibility of understanding this 'discontinuity' in the narrative of their lives, and finding values and beliefs that can accommodate their present experience.

- In pain and away from normal routine, patients often experience increased fear and anxiety and a low sense of well-being. Major **emotional and spiritual** issues can then surface. Chaplaincy helps people to assess their spiritual needs and pain. In a recent survey in Leeds, over 60% of patients claimed to have a religious dimension to their lives. So the appropriateness of such care is not restricted to those who are explicitly religious.

- Illness can also cause people to feel disconnected from traditional sources of **support**. Such distress can have a significant effect on patients. The chaplaincy brings counsel, comfort and support at times of accident, illness or stress. This support extends to relatives as well as to patients.

THE ROLE OF CHAPLAINCY

The chaplains and the visitors who assist them are part of the healing team in the hospital as a whole. They need to be sensitive to the structure within which they work, and play a full part in it. They also need to be pro-active in offering this role, as 'no one goes into hospital to

---

CHAPLAIN

From the Latin word for a 'cloak'. St Martin met a man begging in the rain and without a coat. He could have given the man his own, but then the problem would simply have shifted to himself. So he tore the coat in two – half for the beggar and half for himself. A chaplain is someone who shares support and spiritual protection with others in the storms of life.

---

see a chaplain'. The role therefore needs frequently to be explained and to be advertised.

In particular the role of chaplaincy is:

- to offer care and support 24 hours a day, for patients, relatives and staff
- to help build relationships between staff
- to remind everyone of the spiritual dimension to human existence
- to have a prophetic and questioning role in the areas of ethics, politics and priorities
- to provide public worship and Christian sacraments to staff and patients
- to provide education and training for staff in areas of ethics, spirituality and pastoral care
- to support committed Christian staff in their sense of vocation
- to foster links with local agencies and churches
- to sustain a positive relationship with people of other faiths
- ultimately, to help each person to find peace with themselves, with others, and with God

MODELS OF CHAPLAINCY

Chaplaincy does not operate in the same way in every hospital. A whole-time Anglican chaplain with a large team of visitors will operate very differently from a part-time Baptist or Methodist chaplain working largely on their own. Such part-time chaplains will have less links with staff, and will be able to visit all 'their' patients and spend significant time with them. Because they put their personal ministry to the patient first, part-time chaplains are seen regularly on the wards.

Some whole-time Anglican chaplains will endeavour to see every patient every week, to make an introduction and to offer the sacrament. As the vast majority of patients are 'CofE', that usually means meeting every person admitted to the hospital and allows only a very brief encounter.

Another model is for the chaplain to develop a team of volunteer visitors. This allows the chaplain to ensure each patient is visited, to visit personally in emergencies, and to foster relationships with staff.

Formal religion plays a large part in some chaplaincy programmes – chapel services and administration of the eucharist or anointing with oil. This is of obvious help to those familiar with these 'means of grace'. Many other patients will have a general spiritual awareness but not be active in religious practices. Their spiritual needs are likely to be exacerbated by their illness and hospitalisation, and they are often grateful to be able to explore their feelings in terms of their own understanding of existence. This listening ear, confidential and unquestioning in its acceptance of the patient, is a key element of most chaplaincy work today. It sometimes leads to a greater openness to spiritual things, or a fresh exploration of Christian faith.

TYPICAL CHAPLAINCY?

In a large hospital setting, there may be

- one or two senior chaplains
- one or two assistant chaplains
- a part-time secretary to staff the chaplaincy office
- several part-time chaplains (some Free Church, plus Jewish and Muslim chaplains)
- a team of perhaps 40 or 50 volunteer visitors.

The Chaplaincy Centre may include several offices and a meeting room. There will be a chapel, plus several 'quiet rooms' in different parts of the hospital which people can go for private prayer.

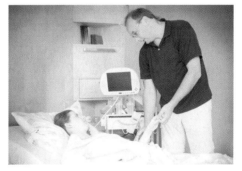

©iStockphoto.com/Claudia Dewald

FURTHER READING

Spiritual Care in the NHS (NAHAT 1998)

A Framework for Spiritual, Faith and Related Pastoral Care (Northern and Yorkshire NHSE, 1996)

BODY AND SPIRIT

Admission to hospital and the experience of serious illness has a levelling effect upon us all. It often provides an opportunity for us to reassess our attitudes to life, our values, our relationships, our morals and our beliefs.

The purpose of chaplaincy is to offer spiritual and social support to patients, as part of the hospital's care for the whole person. By spirituality, we mean the universal search for meaning and purpose which is an inherent part of being human. It is important not to confuse this with 'religion', which is the means by which we organise our spiritual yearnings, the framework within which we make sense of those longings.

> *Spiritual well-being is to say yes to life, in spite of negative circumstances in the context of one's relationship with God, self, community and environment.*
> **National Interfaith Coalition on Ageing**

For patients who regularly attend church, the religious aspects of chaplaincy (such as chapel services, holy communion) are likely to be important points of support, meeting needs normally met through their local church. Some who have 'lapsed' may use the opportunity to get back in touch with their spiritual selves, and may well appreciate the religious side of the chaplaincy's work. Others who have not been to church for years may find these things a comfort, although perhaps only superficially. But for most patients their spiritual needs will have to be addressed without much recourse to religious practices. This will be true of the majority of patients who gave their religion as 'CofE' when they were admitted.

A helpful visit from a chaplaincy Visitor can have a profound effect on someone's well-being, and therefore on their recovery from the particular ailment that has brought them into hospital.

> **Their time in hospital may give the patient the opportunity to put things right with themselves, and a means by which they may come back to God.**

MORE THAN AN ILLNESS

The patient's most pressing spiritual needs may not in fact centre around their illness. They may simply have surfaced in the stressful situation of being admitted to hospital, and the person no longer has the emotional strength to suppress them. Emotional scars that have never been addressed properly may surface during a spell in hospital.

Indeed, their illness may not even be the greatest stress in their lives. Patients come into hospital with a wide range of personal needs:

- the loss of a job (although this is sometimes related to their illness).
- relationship breakdown, with spouse or with children.
- bereavement (although this may also be increasing their fear of death as a result of their own illness).

But all these give avenues into their spiritual lives in the wider sense. We are called to care for the whole person.

SPIRITUAL PAIN

If spirituality is the search for meaning and purpose in our lives, then we will experience 'spiritual pain' when we find that our sense of meaning and purpose is contradicted by our actual experience of life. We have put our faith in one thing, but life is telling us that we were wrong. It is like finding our spouse has been unfaithful to us – we trusted one truth and it turns out to be something else. That hurts.

Spiritual pain is that desolate feeling of meaninglessness, when our view of life and the world around us seems to hit a brick wall. Paul suffered it on the road to Damascus, when he suddenly realised that his zealous persecution of Christians was all horribly wrong – and interestingly he suffered temporary blindness as a result of that painful event. Happily he was able to reassess his life and start again on a new basis.

Similar pain is felt today by:

- the man who has placed his faith in science and medicine, but is now told that there is nothing that medical science can do for him.
- the woman who has believed that if she lives a good life God will reward her, but is now enduring a difficult terminal illness.
- the person whose philosophy is that the material world is all there is, but in facing possible death finds themselves asking 'Why me?' (why not him?) and wistfully wondering whether there is something more.

A suffering person will often make an inward journey questioning the meaning of life, death and human existence; and long-held belief systems may be put to the test. Often they will be found wanting.

EXPRESSIONS OF PAIN

This pain will find expression in a number of forms, and it is important to see behind what is being said and done, to the underlying issues.

Questioning

Why me? What have I done to deserve this? Why doesn't God care about me? Why am I being punished? In fact there are no answers to the questions because the framework of meaning that gave rise to these expectations has broken down. People need help to come to terms with this.

Anger

This is often focused on God, religion and the clergy. It is easy to get drawn into defending God, but this misses the point. We need someone to blame in order to let our anger out. The anger itself is understandable, and people need reassurance about this. They can then look more clearly at who or what has really let them down.

Shame

An illness can activate a deeply-buried sense of being of no value. The person may feel they don't deserve to get better. Some may even feel that if they admit this, the illness may go away (like escaping punishment by admitting you were wrong). Others may question whether it is right to accept the treatment ('such an expensive operation at my age'), or want to keep putting off the decision.

A strong sense of shame can also be felt by people who have had parts of their body removed ('who is going to want me now?'), or who lose control of their bodily functions. It is a small step to believing that God doesn't want them either.

EXTREME SYMPTOMS

Sometimes the pain is all too much, and the person's life seems to collapse:

A sense of hopelessness

People may feel they would be better off dead, or not see any sense in carrying on. They may turn their face to the wall and not want to talk to anyone – what's the point? Their sense of purpose in life has abandoned them. They feel intense emptiness inside.

The world is dying

Everything around them seems to have lost any ability to give them anything. They stop trusting the people who are trying to help. God has disappeared, or God is dead. Everything is crumbling in their hands.

STATISTICS

Taken from the National Survey on Religion in the UK, 2003

- Less than 40% said they believed in God
- 26% said they attended church
- 60% said they had a spirituality

BEING A VISITOR

WHY VISIT?

Why should the chaplaincy consider it useful to pay a call at the bedside of someone who may never have darkened the door of a church, may not be interested in spiritual things, is feelings pretty low, has had umpteen visits that day, and is in need of rest? Certainly the main aim is not to evangelise, or to challenge people with the call to costly discipleship.

Like God

Being a Christian is learning to do what God does. The same root word is used in both the following verses:

- Blessed be the Lord God of Israel, for he has visited and redeemed his people.   (Luke 1:68)
- I was sick and you visited me.
                                        (Matthew 25:36)

We visit people at their point of need because that is what God has done for us in the coming of Christ into the world. We will be judged by how much we have visited those in need, because it is such a God-like action.

Son of encouragement

That's what Joseph, a Levite from Cyprus, was called by the apostles (Acts 4:36). Barnabas was generous with his belongings, but his lasting testimony is that he encouraged other people.

People fall apart not because of the problems they face, but because they become discouraged and lose hope. Patients often suffer the toxic combination of 'I can't cope with all this' and 'no one cares or understands'. Drawing alongside people in simple care and concern can give them courage and hope in their fight to regain their health.

The wider picture

A chaplaincy Visitor is one person with whom a patient can talk about almost anything. Here, as perhaps nowhere else in the system, the patient sets the agenda. Hospital life tends to disempower; a good Visitor can redress some of that balance.

Inner health

The world of the modern hospital is fast-paced and high-tech. It is a frenetic world in which people talk about 'patient outcomes'. Yet within it there is the recognition that people are more likely to prosper if their inner selves are given proper attention. Promoting this inner well-being is a key purpose of modern chaplaincy.

QUALITIES IN A VISITOR

If we are to fulfil these purposes and aims, there are certain key qualities we will need:

Openness

When someone comes to our church as a 'visitor', they meet us on our ground. It is our context and we are at home in it. We welcome them into our familiar territory. That is one form of Christian contact with those outside the church.

Being a chaplaincy Visitor means meeting people (staff and patients) in an unfamiliar setting, with its own norms and expectations. We will work alongside people of various persuasions. They will not conform to us; we need to conform to the setting and live with integrity within it.

Chaplaincy Visitors – like chaplains themselves – are working for the NHS, not for the church. You need to fulfil a spiritual role, but within a secular setting. This calls for an openness of mind and attitude, alongside your own firmly-held Christian convictions.

> *The spiritual aspects of patient care are those aspects of human life relating to experiences that transcend sensory phenomena...*
> *It is often understood as being concerned with meaning and purpose, and for those nearing the end of life, it is commonly associated with the need for forgiveness, reconciliation and affirmation of worth.*
> **World Health Organisation 1990**

Acceptance

We will meet a greater variety of people in a hospital ward than in our day to day lives. Illness is no respecter of persons and brings together the whole range of humanity into one small space. Lonely and vulnerable, they may tell you things they would not have said to you had they met you in the street. They are divulging to doctors and nurses all kinds of private information about themselves – they might confide some such things in you. You will hear things that people don't usually say to you, and you may find some of these things surprising, shocking, unethical, distasteful, or distressing.

Simple acceptance of what is said can have a calming effect on a patient. It can help the conversation go beyond the superficial, to the personal and spiritual realities behind what is being shared. However you may be feeling inside, it is important to communicate your acceptance of whatever is said, as part of your commitment to be alongside people in their difficulty.

It is worth thinking some things through ahead of time. What thoughts and emotions are likely to be stirred up in you by:

- a teenage girl who is going to have an abortion?

- an elderly man who is terminally ill and who just wants to die?

- a young man seriously hurt in a pub brawl?

- a mother of three children angry at the recurrence of her cancer?

Resilience

Many patients will have a straight-forward prognosis and treatment, and your visit to them may be entirely comfortable and enjoyable. But some visits will take all your skills and personal resources to see them through to their conclusion:

- the patient who has just been told there is nothing else that can be done for them, and who is weeping into the bedclothes.

- the father who is facing an operation with only a 50/50 success rate, and who may therefore not be present at his daughter's forthcoming marriage.

- the elderly woman who is coming to terms with the reality that she will have to move into a care home.

Some visits are going to be hard. People need to be able to talk about their inner feelings and fears, and we need to be open to explore these feelings with them. We must not be afraid to talk about illness or its implications, if this is what the patient wants. We must also be able to proceed to the next patient, who may be almost unbearably cheerful.

In one afternoon we may listen to a number of involved stories and become involved in a number of complicated lives. We need to be emotionally fit to cope with this and to continue to be fresh and open with each person.

Presence

The 'bottom line' of being a Visitor is just being there. It is important not to underestimate the value of this in itself, regardless of how little you say or how awkward you may feel.

Having said that, there is a quality to 'being present' with someone, and it is a key quality for those to wish to be Visitors. Being attentive, 'active listening', engaging our whole person with the patient, genuineness – all these kinds of qualities make up our 'presence' with a patient and makes them feel they have been 'visited'.

WANTED AND NEEDED

Being a visitor of the sick is both biblical and on the 'wanted list' of the ward Sister who recognises its importance alongside her bid for the latest model of Intensive Care bed. Within the management of the NHS, the Visitor is low-cost and often very effective. It is a vital 'care and comfort' role which few nurses have time for, and which close relatives (who often need comforting themselves) cannot take on.

DO'S AND DONT'S

Chaplains and chaplaincy visitors will offer:
- unquestioning acceptance
- their availability
- a listening ear
- genuine care
- confidentiality

They will not:
- be judgemental
- impose Christian beliefs on others

A WORD ABOUT WARDS

In practical terms being a Visitor means spending time in that unique building-block of the hospital care system – the 'ward'. It is important to understand how a ward functions, so that you can fit into its pattern of life.

LIFE ON THE WARD

All wards work shift patterns comprising earlies, lates and nights. The shifts will overlap to allow for 'handover'. Do not be surprised if on your second and third visit to a ward, you do not recognise a single face. And do not take it personally when the staff nurse who acted like your long-lost friend one week virtually ignores you the next. Nursing is a pressured job.

©istockphoto.com/Sean Locke

In a short time on a ward it is hard to glean the bigger picture. Wards tend to contain elements of stress, with irritable or awkward patients and personality clashes between staff. At any one point, a ward may be chronically short-staffed, or a well-liked patient may just have died. The ward clerk is a good person to cultivate – they usually know exactly what is going on.

Some points in the day are particularly busy – 'handover' time, meal times, consultants' rounds, ward cleaning. These are key times for chaplaincy Visitors to avoid.

THE PATIENT'S PERSPECTIVE

The patient is no ordinary person. They have been removed from their normal social context, perhaps quite abruptly, and are now immersed in a 'culture' quite alien to them. Even if they have been in hospital before, the world around them is far from normal.

So they will be feeling vulnerable. A lot of strange activity is going on around them, and they have little or no control over any of it. They are sleeping in a strange bed, perhaps in strange bedclothes, probably sharing a ward or bay with several others who are strangers to them. Even if they shut their eyes, everything sounds different. By night they may not be sleeping much, and by day there is a fixed routine that they must fit into. They have become passive, 'patient', steeling themselves to allow things done to them. They have lost control of the most basic things of life – like small children. They are at the mercy of whoever comes to see them (including you). For most people this is not a comfortable way to live, even for a short time.

Often it is also a **boring** world from the patient's point of view. A lot of the activity around them can mean little to them. For a lot of the time there are only strangers to talk to – and most of them are ill. The conversations they do have with relatives and friends tend to centre around their condition. Their world has suddenly shrunk, and the horizons have become the ward itself – now much smaller than before and so with less to see. The only relief may be an occasional foray to X-ray or for a scan, and a visit to the hospital shop may be the highlight of their day. Even a visit to the chapel brings a change of scenery!

Many patients will feel **isolated**. With increasing regionalisation of health care, a patient may be admitted to a hospital some distance from home, especially for more complex conditions or specialised treatment. Relatives may not be able to visit as often as they would like.

They will also feel **tied down**. As a patient, everything comes to you, as if you are rooted to the floor. Nurses, doctors, therapists, dieticians, porters to take you somewhere, housekeepers bring you tea or a meal, the sweet trolley, the book trolley… even the Church!

But there are positive sides to the experience of being a patient. For many there is **relief** that their condition is being treated; indeed they may have waited a long time for admission for treatment. Many express genuine **gratitude** for what is being done for them. There may be **anticipation** about what they will do once they are well again. There may also be some **respite** from other pressures of life, with space to take stock of their lives.

ARRIVING ON A WARD

When you arrive on a ward, try to sense the atmosphere. This comes with practice. In the early stages you will need to fight your own sense of feeling a 'fish out of water' in an unfamiliar environment; and sometimes it will take time to establish yourself as a positive factor in patient health, especially amongst staff who have a more negative view of the church and of the spiritual needs of patients.

Always let the ward staff know you have arrived. There is usually a nurse at the desk. Also ask their advice on how you can best spend your time on the ward. Is there anyone they suggest you see? Anyone they want you to leave undisturbed? If there is someone who has requested a visit, or someone who has been referred to you, ask how they are. Generally every patient will have a 'named nurse' who coordinates all the health care for that patient; it may be appropriate to have a brief conversation with them. It is also courteous to inform the staff when you leave.

APPROACHING THE PATIENT

Remember you are entering their world, so be sensitive to the effect you may be having. Remind yourself of how you feel if someone sits close to you at a favourite spot on a beach or a regular haunt. Their little bit of space within this new and confusing environment has just been invaded – again. It takes time to adjust.

Look for clues about the person. How are they looking? Are there cards and flowers around their bed from many relatives and friends? You can glean a lot about the person simply by being observant. But be careful about making assumptions: who knows whether the perky grandchildren perched on the locker have not just emigrated to Australia? Or whether the many flowers have been sent by sons and daughters too busy to visit so far? But sensitive reference to these things can allow the patient to tell you their story.

You need to introduce yourself as a chaplaincy Visitor, and this may need a little explanation.

It is helpful if you sit down, but ask permission first. It is best to sit on a chair; sitting on the bed raises issues of hygiene.

You need to assess early on how much time to spend with this patient. To a patient 10 minutes may be a very long visit. Influencing factors are:

- the patient's condition. Are they tired? How much effort does talking entail? Is their concentration waning?

- the use the patient is making of the opportunity. Is it being helpful to them to talk to someone who is interested and attentive, but not involved in their medical care?

- whether others at the bedside welcome your presence.

- whether you feel you have something appropriate to offer to this particular situation.

©istockphoto.com/Alexandru Kacso

KNOWING WHAT TO SAY

Many prospective Visitors may be anxious about what to say and worried that they will 'dry up' in this strange environment. Others will find it all too easy to talk, and need to be wary of the pitfalls. Know yourself, and go prepared to have helpful conversations with patients. You then create a context within which your care for the patient can take place.

QUESTIONS

Avoid asking a lot of questions – patients get bombarded with questions all day, and can do without more interrogation by a Visitor! Be sensitive in the questions you do ask, and avoid asking about their medical condition. Also avoid asking 'How are you?' – if they were fine they would not be here!

'Open' questions are good for getting the conversation going:

- How are things going for you today?
- What did you think of the outing from the ward yesterday?

Such questions give the patient the opportunity to respond in any way they want. 'Closed' questions invite a simple yes or no answer, and you are no further forward.

LISTENING

You can sustain the conversation by picking up on whatever the patient says. This shows you are listening, and gives them encouragement to elaborate.

- So the outing was fun…
- You seem to have enjoyed that holiday – I suppose there was something special about it…
- It sounds like that was difficult / a relief / a demanding time …

Topics of conversation will range wide and far. It can often be helpful to ask where the person is from, and invite them to talk about their home and area. This can give clues about their feelings about being away from their home.

Make sure you listen to the feelings as well as the information. Empathy means discovering and sharing someone else's feelings and viewpoint regardless of your own. Listen to their behaviour as well as their words.

Let them talk about what they want to talk about. You do not need to know details about them, or collect standard information. It may be helpful to say that you know nothing about their medical condition, and are offering friendship and support as part of their recovery.

ACCEPTING EMOTIONS

When people share difficult feelings, they are looking for an empathetic response. They need to know that you sense their difficult feeling, and that you are willing to be there with them as they feel it. It is important to convey that we are comfortable in this role, and that we can absorb the difficult emotions without embarrassment. If you find what has been said difficult yourself, you need to resist the temptation to change the subject.

Our role is not to jolly people along, or deflect them from their difficulties, or to offer platitudes, especially religious ones. Jesus showed signs of great stress in Gethsemane as he contemplated his own suffering and death. The patient's difficult feelings are probably entirely proper in their situation, but the person is likely to need our reassurance about this. Otherwise you will find a rapid drying of eyes, attempts at self-composure, abject apologies – and the moment is lost, along with a little bit of trust.

Sometimes all that is required is simply being there, perhaps quietly holding a hand, allowing the patient to talk openly whatever the crisis, and to be a support in their need.

Some patients will be angry. Often there is a sense of unfairness, of a tragedy undeserved. Some will want to blame God for their experiences. Do not try to stop or curtail this kind of expression of emotion. Such anger is a natural part of coming to terms with any kind of 'loss', and a greater acceptance will come in due course. It is generally helpful to go along with the sense of unfairness but gently to challenge any perception of 'being punished'. Don't be unduly protective of God; He is big enough to absorb whatever is thrown at Him – as Jesus did on the cross.

PITFALLS

Be careful of any comment that may put pressure or expectations on the patient. 'Hurry up and get better' can merely leave people with a sense of guilt at their lack of progress. Do not try to predict the course of a person's illness and recovery.

Avoid talking about your own illnesses or operations, or making comparisons with your own experience. It can be helpful to mention that you had a similar experience – it provides common grounds and can offer some reassurance – but get quickly back to centring on the patient. If they really want to know about your experience, they will ask.

Beware of questions that may come over as being 'nosy'. Before pursuing some information, ask yourself, 'For whose benefit am I asking?' Stay with the patient's needs, and try to give them openings to talk about what would be helpful to them to share with someone.

While you give the patient your full attention, be careful not to stare! This is particularly threatening when the patient is a 'captive audience'.

You don't have to be talking all the time. Short silences can be creative, and some patients will not share anything significant without them.

©istockphoto.com

DON'T...

- argue with a patient, especially about religion
- show shock or disapproval of anything that the patient says
- tell the patient what they must do
- compare their condition with someone else's
- preach a sermonette
- try to convert the patient
- tell them they have done the wrong thing
- make promises that you can't keep

NOTES

GOOD VISITING PRACTICE

PRAYER

Pray for yourself before you start. You may want to use the Chapel. Hand your pre-occupations over to God, and ask for sensitivity to His Spirit and for the gifts He knows you will need for this time.

Pray for patients that you visit. Many patients will be pleased to know that you will pray for them, but only make promises that you can keep.

- I'll pray for you in the Chapel before I leave.
- I'll pray for you on the day of your operation.

Pray for people the prayers that they don't have the faith or hope to pray for themselves. Pray on your own or with the chaplaincy team; it is not appropriate to bring patient needs and concerns to church-based prayer meetings.

At the end of the visit, you need to judge whether to offer to **pray with the patient**. Certainly you should only do so with the patient's permission. Always give them an opt out – they are trapped in bed and cannot walk away from you! Keep your prayer short. Use enough volume to be heard but not too loud. You might ask the patient to suggest what they would most like to ask God for. Keep it simple, and try to use words and phrases that the patient

has used to describe their thoughts and feelings.

You could also **encourage patients to pray for themselves**. Some patients appreciate the gift of a prayer card, to help them in this, the chaplaincy will have a supply of appropriate ones. The patient can be encouraged by noting that illness proves to be a time of real spiritual growth for many people. But don't underestimate the difficulties of praying amid the anxiety, anger and sometimes despair of being a patient. Be prepared to listen before pointing people to the spiritual resource of prayer.

If people feel unable to pray for themselves, encourage them to pray for the staff who are caring for them. Or they could pray for their relatives who are worried about them; or about some relationships which have been neglected and need repair. This can help to move the focus of prayer away from themselves and their anxieties.

OTHER FAITHS

Particular sensitivity is needed when visiting people of another faith. It would be appropriate to check that a Muslim patient has the contact they want with their Imam, and the chaplaincy office should be able to refer them to an official chaplain appropriate to their religious faith. But remember that you are part of an NHS hospital team, not a representative of the Christian Church as such. So you can also be solicitous about their personal and spiritual needs: are their dietary needs being met? Have they space for their prayers? What about 'modesty' needs? Don't immediately assume that this person is someone else's responsibility.

BODY LANGUAGE

The way you present yourself physically to the patient will say a lot – perhaps not the things you intend to say. So it is worth giving attention to your posture, to avoid misunderstanding. In particular, it is easy for the patient to feel 'hemmed in' by your

---

FOUR LEVELS OF THE SPIRIT

How am I relating to…

…myself?
Issues of self-esteem, sense of purpose, unresolved feelings of guilt, fear or abandonment.

…others?
Family, friends, community, meaningful relationships. Issues of isolation, loneliness, unresolved grief.

…the world?
Environment, global concerns, creation, violence and peace. Issues of self-worth, need to be needed, vocation.

…God?
Divinity, universe, higher power, eternity. Issues of acceptance, guilt, anxiety, despair.

presence; so make sure you sit down and that the patient can see beyond you.

The patient may be checking you out to see whether you are someone to be trusted with their 'story'. You may feel relaxed sitting back in the chair with your arms crossed or your hands in your pockets, but this can convey disinterest in the patient. Better to sit slightly forward, clearly attentive, using nods and facial expressions to show you are listening. Beware of the stifled yawn (if you are tired, take a break), and the furtive glance at the watch (does it really matter what time it is?). Eye contact is important, but don't stare continuously; try to meet the patient's gaze when they look at you.

Touch can be helpful, especially with very ill patients or those who have difficulty communicating. A simple holding of a hand can get through to someone who is lost for words, and sometimes patients will initiate this, offering you their hand to hold. But be sensitive, and look out for the hand that withdraws, perhaps under the bedclothes; if in doubt, don't.

PACING YOURSELF

Many visits will be enjoyable, even superficial. Sometimes a patient will have a tale of deep personal tragedy to tell you. Whatever your round of visits hold for you that day, it is important to arrive at each patient fresh and ready to give them your whole attention.

With smaller wards these days it is easier to take a break unobtrusively – to digest a demanding set of visits, take stock of your feelings, or even to take some notes. So pace yourself. After completing one bay, you could walk off the ward for a few minutes or sit in the day room. If you feel mentally drained after a deep and difficult personal encounter, give yourself some space. You owe it to the next person you visit. If you need someone to 'off-load' onto, go and see the chaplain.

TAKING NOTES

Even while you are talking with a patient, it may be appropriate to make a note of something – especially something you have said you will do to follow up the visit. This shows the seriousness with which you take it – like the medical staff taking notes to coordinate care.

Otherwise, your taking of notes will be done after your visits. Certainly make enough notes to jog your memory next week if the patient is still in. Note any particular needs, especially if the person ought to be followed up by the chaplain. If questions are asked about your visit, you should be able to give an account of it. If it was a particularly hard visit, or did not go well, you might want to discuss it with the chaplain as part of your supervision.

Also keep notes on your own feelings and thoughts, as this will help your self-awareness and will develop your ability to cope with difficult situations.

HOW TO LEAVE

Leave positively. Hopefully your presence has been a blessing to the patient; you can also bless them by leaving at the right time! The 'ministry of absence' is the art of knowing when a visit has done what it can do, and having the courage and confidence to get up and go. Beware of giving the impression that you are leaving because you have other people to see; this may sound innocuous but it communicates a lack of concern. You are leaving because you have done what you came to do for the patient.

THE COMFORTING VISITOR

The patient seeks someone who will:

- understand
- accept their emotions
- come alongside them
- be sensitive to their mood changes
- allow them to set their own pace as they move from denial to acceptance
- not need comforting by the patient

As busy, active, relevant people, we want to earn our bread by making a real contribution ... doing something to show that our presence makes a difference. And so we ignore our greatest gift, which is our ability to be there to listen and to enter into solidarity with those who suffer.
Henri Nouwen

ON CONFIDENTIALITY

BAD EXAMPLES

A manager of a small Midlands company attended a service at his local church. He heard prayers for one of his work colleagues (using his full name) who in the words of the bidding was 'seriously ill and needing further major investigations'. He mentioned his genuine concern for the sick person to the company personnel officer. A few months after his return to work, the person was made redundant as part of a general down-sizing of the company. A suspicion remained that the possibility of expensive sickness payments may have been part of the company's decision to choose this person for redundancy.

> **Are any among you sick? they should call for the elders of the church…**
> James 5:14

A hospital Visitor was making a rare visit to a distant hospital to follow up a patient.

On the ward they recognised a man from their own congregation, and returned to tell their minister that the man was in hospital for cancer tests. The minister in turn visited the man's wife, to support her in this difficult situation – only to find that the fact her husband was in hospital at all was news to her. She was already in a fragile mental and nervous condition, and the shock precipitated her breakdown and her admission to the local acute psychiatric clinic. Aware of his wife's delicate condition, the husband had in fact arranged to 'go away on business for a few days' rather than worry her with the truth about the investigations.

Both these are real situations. And both underline the critical need for confidentiality in relation to people who are ill.

MORE THAN DISCRETION

Health care today is highly complex and has considerable knock-on effects in various aspects of a person's private life. Everyone who works in the hospital setting must safeguard the interests of patients by preserving confidentiality and protecting patient privacy.

This is not just a matter of good practice; it is a matter of law, and NHS staff (including chaplains) can be dismissed for a breach in the regulations. The document *Confidentiality – Use and Disclosure of Personal Health Information* (Department of Health, 1994) states (sections 4.32 and 4.29):

> If approached by a third party (including representatives of the media or anyone thought to be contributing information to the media), neither NHS bodies nor anyone who works in the NHS should confirm that any individual is a patient, or divulge any information about his or her condition, without the patient's consent.

> Hospitals should, when registering patients, record religious persuasion where the patient is willing to disclose this. This information may be passed on

---

GOOD CARE

The following norms of good pastoral care are taken from Standards of Practice in Pastoral Care, published by the Anglican Association of Advisers in Pastoral Care and Counselling.

- to avoid harming the recipient by what is done or not done.

- to acknowledge that the relationship between carer and recipient is at that time a-symmetrical and unequal… No advantages (personal, sexual or financial) should accrue to the carer from the relationship… other than the satisfaction and fulfilment which belong to the carer knowing that the work has been done for the benefit of the recipient.

- to work in such a way that the individual's or family's context, culture and social group are always taken into account with skill and respect.

- to maintain rigorously the principle of confidentiality within limits that are agreed in advance with the recipient.

- to gain the recipient's informed consent before embarking on actions on his/her behalf.

- to maintain one's knowledge and skill at the level appropriate to maintaining competent caring and to be clear as to the limits of one's competency.

- to enable recipients to be free to disengage from one's services and/or from a relationship with one at any time.

to the appropriate hospital chaplain or religious leader, where that person is a member of the hospital staff, unless the patient has refused permission for this. Information about a patient may not be passed to any religious organisation or its members outside the NHS without the patient's consent.

Several things are clear from these regulations:

- The very fact that someone is a patient is confidential information.
- The condition someone is suffering from is also confidential.
- Only the patient has the right to say who may be told and when, outside those professionally involved in their care.
- Family, friends, employers, neighbours, clergy and fellow members of churches and other faith groups, cannot be given such information without the express permission of the patient.

Hospital Visitors work in the context of the NHS and are subject to its regulations. As a Visitor, you will be expected to observe confidentiality just as strictly as other members of staff, and your failure to do so will almost certainly result in the loss of your position.

THE WIDER PICTURE

Such regulations are not just important for patients. They affect the way our society works and in particular our ability to control infections and illnesses.

A pertinent example is HIV and AIDS, which gives rise to irrational adverse attitudes from many people in society, Christians included. Once confidentiality about a patient's condition is breached, there are often major damaging results for the patient in relation to employment, insurance, pensions and mortgages. Without the assurance of confidentiality, people will be slow to come forward to receive the treatment and counselling they and their families need. This is likely to lead to the further spread of the condition.

> The material on confidentiality on these pages is abstracted from the article 'Whose Business? Respect for Confidentiality and Privacy in the Provision of Pastoral Care for Patients at Home or in Hospital' by Robert Clark, from *Ministry Today* Vol 6, pages 14-19.

MEDICAL QUESTIONS

Sometimes a patient may ask the Visitor questions about their medical condition. Although this sounds surprising, there are a number of reasons why it sometimes happens:

- they find it really hard to raise the question with anyone. At an unconscious level the patient may be 'practising asking' by posing the question to someone they realise does not know the answer.
- they have come to trust the Visitor, and so ask the question they cannot ask the medical staff – sometimes to their own surprise.
- they have been given bad news about their condition, and are looking for reassurance that things will be all right in the end.
- they do not trust the information they have received, and they suspect that the Visitor may have been given some inside information.

You may be tempted to give some reassurance, but this is to be resisted as you do not know the condition of the patient or the possible outcome of their illness. Even if you have knowledge of this particular illness (e.g. from your own experience or that of friends), such knowledge may be out of date. It is anyway not

your job to give medical information to the patient, even if you have it.

Explain that you are a volunteer chaplaincy Visitor, and that you do not know the answers to medical questions. You know no more than the general public about medical matters, even though you work within the hospital setting. Some patients will persist with their questions, and it may take some determination to hold your ground.

Discuss with the patient how they can get the answers to their questions. In particular, the patient may appreciate talking through with you just who they are going to ask – perhaps the Ward Sister or the Consultant. Give the patient the opportunity of outlining to you what they are going to ask and when. Usually this works, and you will find on a subsequent visit that the patient did ask and got their answer. They may or may not want to tell you what answer they got and you need to respect that.

Occasionally a patient will ask you to ask the nursing staff to talk to them about their question. But it is preferable for the patient to take the initiative having talked it over with you first. Once over the hurdle of this question, they are then more able to ask further questions to appropriate staff in the future.

IS IT FOR ME?

KEY QUALIFICATIONS

The kind of person who has the potential to be an effective chaplaincy Visitor is likely to have the following characteristics:

- **responsible**: able to keep to a weekly commitment, keep confidences, and be accountable to the chaplains through supervision

- **stable**: fit enough emotionally to listen to the cares of others, has good personal support from family and friends, can function on their own in demanding situations

- **friendly**: can relate simply and warmly in a relaxed manner, can get along with a wide range of people

- **self-aware**: knows how difficulties in life have affected them, can use this to help them draw alongside others

- **devout**: has a lively Christian faith with habits of private prayer and public worship, able to speak of their faith however simply

- **loyal**: able to act as part of a team, work cooperatively with medical staff and the chaplains

- **astute**: perceptive about people and about situations, able to put these into words in notes and for referral to others

Chaplaincy visiting is not a suitable activity for those who:

- are in poor health themselves, because the role is quite demanding

- feel a need to be wanted, because frequently they won't be wanted and they must be able to handle that

- are seeking an avenue for sharing the gospel with others, because this is mostly a caring rather than a sharing ministry

- are unduly serious, because a sense of humour helps a lot

In applying for a position as a Visitor, it is important that you disclose any previous convictions. The post of chaplaincy Visitor is not exempt from the provisions of Section 4(2) of the Rehabilitation of Offenders Act (1974), and so you are not entitled to withhold information about convictions which for other purposes are 'spent' under the provisions of the Act. Disclosure of an offence will not necessarily be a barrier to becoming a Visitor, and information given in your application will be held in confidence. If your work involves contact with children or vulnerable adults, your police record will be checked on the police computer.

> *Is this you? Write some reflections here.*

A CHURCH THAT HEALS

PURPOSE

This Unit describes how the healing work of Christ can be expressed through the life of the local church. Special emphasis is put on the knowledge, skills and attitudes required of those who take part in this ministry.

CONTENTS

Why do it?   70
A healing church   72
Teach us to pray   74
Healing in worship   76
Healing toolkit   78
Channels of healing   82

WHY DO IT?

Before we consider how to engage in a healing ministry in the local church setting, it is important to pause and ask why we are doing it in the first place. Many who wish to start a healing ministry, or become involved in one, do so with a mixture of motives. It is important that you understand yours, because what you carry in your heart is usually (either by word or deed) conveyed to the people with whom you pray for God's healing touch.

POOR MOTIVATION

The motivation for having a healing ministry should **not be**...

...to bring in renewal

Some hope to bring a rather 'sleepy' church alive by beginning a healing ministry within it. Surely if healing begins to happen, then the whole of this church's spiritual life will take off!

Although this has sometimes happened, it is really working the wrong way round. Healing is a *result* of spiritual renewal, not vice versa. You cannot force a dynamic healing ministry on a church which needs to learn to be more open to God first. Each church needs to find a style of prayer for healing that parallels its present point of growth and development. And it needs a style of healing ministry it can live with – as opposed to one it can't!

YOUR STYLE

Think for a few minutes about what style of healing ministry might be appropriate for your church.

Which of your current church services might it fit into? Is it best to have it at a Communion service, or not? Where in the service would you put it? And why?

Then compose a simple prayer for healing, appropriate for any person in your church who may come.

...to experience power

If you read Acts and then look at your local church, it is not hard to sense that one is a rather weak reflection of the other. Surely if healing begins to happen, then the power of Christ will be clearly demonstrated in our day!

We must be careful that we do not become a member of the church's healing team in order to feel significant and chase illusions of being powerful. The most effective people in the healing ministry tend to be those who are aware of their limitations and problems, and who know that God does not call them on the basis of their natural strengths – but their weaknesses.

We need to take care to resist the temptation to adopt a dynamic *style* in the hope of acquiring more spiritual power. There are quiet ways of finding the healing touch of Christ, and it is important not to denigrate them. The most powerful healings can happen in silence, without there being any disclosure of the problems or needs concerned.

CARE AND OBEDIENCE

Our involvement in Christian healing begins with God and not us. Christ commissioned his disciples to preach the good news and to demonstrate the kingdom power of God, including specific instructions about healing (Luke 9:1-2, 10:9). The prime motivation for taking up the task of healing the sick should be obedience.

This is actually quite freeing and energising. How many of us debate whether we have enough faith to pray for someone's healing? Or perhaps we question whether God really will heal a person – or even wants to, especially if they are near to death. Faith is important, but it is not of prime importance in the motivation to pray for healing.

The healing ministry must not be entered into as a means to another end. We do it because Christ calls us to love and care for the world, including care for people's physical and emotional health. We use whatever means he chooses to put at our disposal to achieve this. With all my skills and gifts of loving care, I share in the journey of someone else's healing, and leave the consequences of my obedience to God. This is not being passive – it is a dynamic commitment to continue to pray while not having all the answers.

COUNTING THE COST

Jesus caused as much conflict by what he did as by what he said. His miracles of healing aroused the hostility of the ruling powers, who then plotted against him. We may experience the same. So we need to be clear about our motivation, because involvement in the healing ministry may be costly and we need to be certain that it is worthwhile.

More pain

The hardest question to answer in the healing ministry is 'why?'. Why are some healed and not others? Sometimes there may be a very good reason why someone is not healed. More often there is no apparent reason, and we are plunged into the pain of not knowing why. We can be tempted to invent reasons – to make ourselves (and possibly the person we are trying to help) feel better. Before getting involved in the healing ministry, we should ask ourselves if we can live with not knowing why some are healed and others not.

Being vulnerable

The work of healing is not the powerful caring for the weak. The more we enter the field of care and prayer, the more we become aware of our own limitations and woundedness. We realise that we require prayer for ourselves. We will learn and be challenged by the brave and difficult journeys of those we pray with.

We will also have to come to terms with our own problems on the way, and not hide behind a mask of serenity when all

within us is crying out for answers. Trying to understand the mystery and mess surrounding the healing ministry is a taxing business.

A spiritual battle

Christian healing is not recovering one's health in order to go back to the old life as if nothing has changed. Embedded in the work of healing is a spiritual message – that the Kingdom of God is moving forward and that Jesus is active in our world. It is an invitation to live healthily in the will of God and to come under the rule of Christ. This includes the healing of our relationship with God.

Many want healing but resist or reject the way of Christ. We must be aware of the spiritual battle surrounding the healing ministry, and those who pray for the sick must take this issue seriously.

LINKED IN?

Think of a number of ways in which your church is already a healing resource in the community. For example, the church may pray regularly for members of the medical and caring professions, or the premises may be used by people with special needs.

If you can, share your ideas with someone else, and listen to their ideas.

How will a specific 'healing ministry' relate to these other activities?

Christ has no body now on earth but yours,
No hands but yours, no feet but yours.
Yours are the eyes through which he must look out in compassion on the world.
Yours are the feet with which he is to go about doing good.
Yours are the hands with which he must bless men now.

St Teresa of Avila

A HEALING CHURCH

If healing is going to form an integral part of the life of a local church, great care needs to be taken to establish it on a solid foundation. The beginnings of a healing ministry may occasionally come 'out of the blue', but typically it takes place within a wider framework. The long-term effects of a healing ministry will depend on how solid this framework is.

THE FOUNDATIONS

The foundations are the parts you don't see most of the time, but they are essential if the building is not to fall down.

The wisdom of God. In the Scriptures God teaches us what to expect as we pray for healing. It is important that we read these carefully and prayerfully, seeking to understand not only *what* God has done in the past but also *why*. The more we understand the mind of God and his purposes in bringing healing to individuals,

the more we will be able to engage with the healing ministry today with perceptiveness and Godly wisdom.

The authority of Christ. We have Christ's commission to engage in the work of healing. Healing is not something we do – it is *his* work. Having a share in that work flows naturally from our status of belonging to God's family, adopted by grace because of the work of Christ. The authority we have is not based on how strong our faith is or how able we are, but on the fact that Christ calls us to work alongside him.

The power of the Spirit. Power speaks of God's divine energy to accomplish his will. The Spirit is also the presence of Christ in our midst, strengthening and encouraging us to fulfil all he commanded us to do. If we have power without God's wisdom and authority, we **blow up**. But if we have wisdom and authority without the power of the Spirit, we **slow up**! If we can hold all these together, then by God's grace we will **grow up**.

THE STEPS UP

There are also important steps to take before we enter the building proper. These are things to do before starting a healing ministry. Many healing ministries have been wrecked because the church was not ready for its introduction.

Teaching. Only a small number of people may be involved in running a healing service or in praying with the sick, but the whole church needs to understand this important part of its life. So teaching about Christian healing needs to involve the whole church. That means incorporating it into the normal programme of teaching and preaching.

Training. In a sense the healing ministry can only be learned 'on

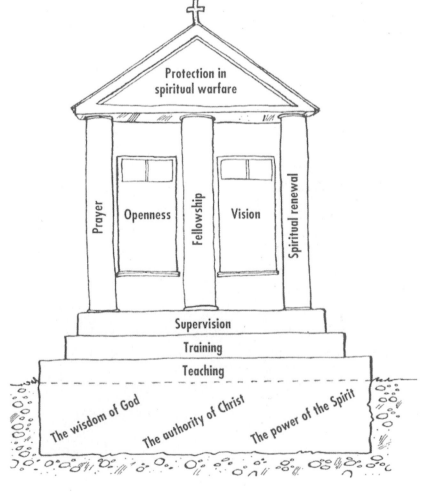

the job', but some essential training should be done before someone is involved in prayer for healing (such as this workbook).

Supervision. Before you start, put in place the mechanisms by which you will assess how the work is going, what problems there are, and how the work should develop and improve.

PILLARS OF SUPPORT

Many things are important but some things are essential if the building is to stay up, especially when life gets 'stormy'. These are like the pillars of an ancient building, or the metal framework of a modern office block.

Prayer. We are called and instructed in Scripture to pray, and any worthwhile work for God will be soaked in prayer. In our prayers for the healing work of Christ to be worked out in our church, we will often be stripped down and made more aware of God's will and purposes. Thus in prayer the practice and direction of our healing ministry will be sharpened. Those who are not directly involved in the healing ministry also have a part to play in prayer support, and in the discernment that often comes with it.

Fellowship. A healing ministry can easily become the preserve of an elite group in the church. It can then become divisive and break down the fellowship of the believers. The ministry of healing belongs to the whole church, and must be practised with the agreement and continued support of the church as a whole. Sustaining the fellowship of the church is an essential ingredient in the long-term health and healing that Christ longs to see.

Spiritual renewal. The work of healing must continually be refreshed and empowered by the touch of God. In Acts the apostles received the filling of the Spirit on a number of occasions, followed usually by a renewed experience of healing. On occasions the whole church should be invited to receive prayer for the touch of God on its life, including the renewal of its work of healing.

SAFE FROM THE ELEMENTS

If the roof is weak or leaking, then even the strongest and best appointed house will soon be in ruins. These are just 'natural' forces at work. But if our church is demonstrating the power of God at work to save and heal the lost and diseased, it will draw the attention of the spiritual opposition – the spiritual 'elements' that are set against God and his work (Galatians 4:3). We need to protect the work of healing, and pray against discouragement and the temptation to become unbalanced. This will involve good pastoral care, promotion of our spiritual health, and holiness of life.

ONGOING MAINTENANCE

Even the best house needs looking after – like painting or replacing windows. And our healing ministry will need constant attention to ensure it continues to follow what the Spirit is saying to the church.

Openness is needed, as different needs arise and may need to be met in new ways. This can be hard when some people have invested a lot of themselves in one style of healing ministry, and change may feel like a personal threat.

Vision is important if we are to avoid the temptation just to try new things. We need to listen carefully to any new direction in which God may be taking us.

NOTES

TEACH US TO PRAY

There are lots of books written on prayer. But when we come to prayer for healing, we all tend to feel like the disciples asking Jesus, 'Lord, teach us to pray'. We feel we need to learn to pray as he did, if we are to act in the power of God as he did. This is a feeling to be trusted...

MARY AND MARTHA

A useful model is the 'prayer' Mary and Martha used when their brother Lazarus was very ill and in danger of dying (John 11:30):

'Lord, the one you love is sick.'

First, they turned their minds to Jesus, and in doing so they acknowledged his authority. Then they affirmed Christ's love for the one they brought to him in healing intercession. Only thirdly did they indicate what Lazarus' need was.

So often we do this in the wrong order and with the wrong emphasis. We begin by dwelling on the sickness. Then we plead for healing, as though love has to be coaxed from a reluctant saviour. We may hardly find time at all to affirm the authority and the healing power of Jesus.

The heart of healing prayer lies in the practice of the presence of the Risen Christ. We bring ourselves and those in need into his presence. We rest in his will, his power and his goodness. We should feel refreshed rather than drained by our prayers.

We call it prayer.
God calls it listening.

THE LORD'S PRAYER

The Lord's Prayer is a useful framework of thought in praying for healing:

- God is a loving father, desiring the best for his children.
- What matters most is that God's kingly rule is expressed and his purposes fulfilled.
- We need to look to him for the fulfilling of our most basic needs in life.
- We are people who need forgiveness, and who extend that same forgiveness to others.
- We need to be aware that our own sinfulness can block healing both for ourselves and for others.

JESUS IN ACTION

If we look at some of the healing stories in the gospels, we become aware of some of the ingredients in Jesus' response.

Look at the passages below and write down:

- what do you observe about the person in need, as they engage with Jesus?
- how did Jesus approach this person or responded to them?
- what was Jesus' prayer for them, or what did he do for them?

Mark 1:40-45
-
-
-

Mark 2:1-12
-
-
-

Mark 5:25-34
-
-
-

Mark 10:46-52
-
-
-

Four themes emerge from this:

1. Jesus listened

He took on board what people actually said to him, and heard people who were sidelined by others. He also 'listened' to the needs of those who said nothing, whose needs were expressed in actions rather than words.

2. Jesus asked

Jesus invited a blind person to be specific about what he wanted. He did not assume. He drew out a woman who had been healed into the public gaze with a question. For other famous clarifying questions, see Mark 5:9, 9:21, John 5:6.

3. Jesus forgave

Proclaiming forgiveness was integral to the ministry of Jesus. Sometimes it is specifically linked to healing; mostly it is seen as a complementary part of his ministry.

Giving and receiving forgiveness is part of what makes us whole. Before someone can grow in wholeness, God may ask them to let go of some hurt or powerful feelings or inner vows made in response to pain inflicted by others. Unwillingness to forgive stands as a block within many lives. Jesus calls us to choose life and freedom, and freely forgave those who were trapped by sin themselves.

4. Jesus challenged

He challenged the woman's secrecy. He challenged the onlookers' unwillingness to forgive and to release others from misery. In deliverance, he challenged the powers that kept people in bondage. He was not afraid of confrontation in order to bring out the full implications of the healing.

THE POINT OF NEED

It is easy to feel that prayer for healing is a special activity, quite different from our other prayers and different in character from the rest of our Christian discipleship. This is not so. A simple definition of prayer for healing (by Morris Maddocks) is:

> 'Christian healing is Jesus Christ meeting me at the point of my need.'

We can pray for people in this way, whether or not they have a specific need of 'healing'.

You can practice this kind of prayer with a friend. Sit quietly together, and each of you open your hearts to God and invite him to make you aware of your need for today. After a few minutes, share those needs with each other. If there are several, clarify the need by asking what is the most important part of the need now?'

Then reflect back to each other what you have 'heard' your needs to be. If that is clear, pray simply for each other. You could just pray, 'Jesus Christ bring his healing to your point of need.' You can pray this prayer without even knowing what the other person's need is.

This is a useful way to begin to pray for healing. It is a foundational way of praying, and can be used by the whole congregation. We need to have confidence that Jesus will meet people at their point of need. As we experience that this is the case, then we will grow in our trust of him and have more confidence when faced with situations which challenge our faith.

A PRAYER OF PREPARATION

We praise you that you alone are the God who heals.

As we wait on you now, may your Holy Spirit come upon us and make us aware of the most important need that we carry in our hearts.

We promise you that what you reveal we will offer to your Son Jesus Christ so that he can bring your healing to our need.

Watch over this time of prayer and grant us your protection and power to heal.

So come Holy Spirit and glorify the Father as Jesus brings his healing presence among us.

INSIGHT?

Sometimes we get insight into someone's situation when we listen to them and pray with them. This can be shared with the other person in an open and unthreatening way. It is seldom the whole picture, but it may give them insight into their own situation which can help them in their prayers and in their discipleship.

HEALING IN WORSHIP

There are several ways of bringing prayers for healing into the worship life of the local church.

THE INTERCESSIONS

Intercessory prayers, including prayers for the sick, are said at most services. There are ways in which these can be made more specific and effective. For example:

- praying in small groups for about five minutes. Here the needs of the sick can be shared and prayed for, and many more people involved.

- keeping a record of answered prayers, and sharing these within the intercessions to encourage people to continue to pray with faith.

- processional prayer, where people write down a prayer for someone who is sick, and (perhaps during a hymn) process to the front and place their prayer on the table or altar. The minister can conclude with a general prayer, perhaps lifting up the written prayers.

- keeping an intercessions book, in which the congregation is invited to write the names of those who are ill; this is then lifted up before God during the intercessions, as a way of praying for those written in it.

CHURCH NOTICES

1st Sunday
   Sung eucharist with processional prayers for healing

2nd Sunday
   Morning Worship with laying on of hands

3rd Sunday
   Family eucharist with prayer ministry

4th Sunday
   Healing service, with guest preacher

5th Sunday
   Quiet prayers for healing

BRIDGE SERVICES

A special service of prayer or thanksgiving can be held for all those involved in healing in the community. This would include doctors, nurses, social workers, counsellors and others. Members of all these professions could be invited. Members of the congregation who fulfil one of these roles could be interviewed and prayed for specifically. There can be special prayers for the health and wellbeing of the community as a whole, as well as for individuals.

LAYING ON OF HANDS

This is usually administered at the front of church, often during the administration of communion or immediately after the service. There are two ways of doing this:

- the recipient is given the opportunity to say why healing is needed. This is often followed by extended extempore prayer, in which the Holy Spirit is invited to respond to the need expressed. This can be more personal and gives opportunity for the Holy Spirit to determine the form of ministry. It can be very effective, but it can also go badly wrong. The Holy Spirit is not always in charge!

- no enquiry is made about the reason why ministry is being sought. A short standard prayer is said for each person. This can be less threatening, as people are not expected to give a reason for coming forward. It also takes the focus away from the ailment itself and onto the presence of the healing Christ. But it can become mechanical and impersonal, leaving people feeling uncared for.

Sometimes the whole congregation can be invited to 'lay hands' on each other, by holding hands with the person on either side. Each then becomes both the recipient and the ministrant, and after a period of silence, all can say a prayer of healing together. In a communion service, this could take place at The Peace. This practice can helpfully draw in many people who would never have asked for the laying on of hands, or offered to minister it.

It is good for a wide range of people to be involved in the laying on of hands, both clerical and lay, so that it is clear that this is a ministry of the Body of Christ and not just of an elite few within it.

SPECIAL HEALING SERVICES

There are some good reasons for holding occasional services specifically to allow the healing work of Christ to take place.

- they give visibility to the Church's healing ministry, in an age when belief in prayer for healing has largely died out. This public testimony may be important in the Church's relations with the wider community, especially its health care professionals.

- they ensure that healing is not kept on the sidelines of the Church's ministry. They focus that work, just as a 'mission' can focus the on-going work of evangelism.

- in practice, they are often great spiritual events and can draw out a deeper sense of faith within the congregation – and indeed within those who minister.

The aim of a healing service is to practice the presence of Christ and to allow him to bring healing in and through all present. We can expect strengthening and blessing. We can also expect that people will be helped and healed in tangible ways. Often these will be explicable; occasionally they will not be and it will not be inappropriate to speak of 'miracles'.

Preaching is an essential ingredient in a healing service. This should aim to communicate the reality of Jesus. This does not need to be based on a healing story from one of the Gospels. There is much to be said for using the passages appointed for the day, because the Bible as a whole is a book about healing, about the restoration of wholeness at many levels in life – body, mind, spirit, attitudes, relationships and lifestyle. Healing is also corporate as well as individual, and concerned with eternity as well as time.

COME TOGETHER

In the Christian musical 'Come Together', people who have received a certain healing are asked to stand as a testimony to what God has done for them. They then remain standing as those who are seeking the same healing are also asked to stand as a testimony of what they are seeking from God. The first group are then invited to meet aside and pray with the second group and pray that God would bring to others the healing he has already given to them.

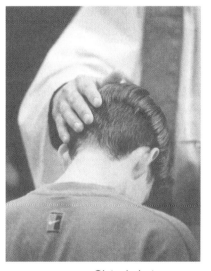

©istockphoto.com

CHRIST-TINGLES?

What should we expect to 'feel' when we pray with someone for healing? Some people experience a tingling sensation in their hands, and recipients may have feelings of unusual heat or something like an electric shock. People report other similar phenomena.

Stress should not be laid on these things. Healing can take place where none of these things happen, and can fail to take place when they do. It can be harmful and distracting if we put our faith in feelings and experiences such as these, rather than in the Lord himself.

Ministrants may experience a natural tiredness afterwards, but there should also be a sense of refreshment rather than being drained, because it is Jesus who does the healing work. We are merely his channels. Recipients should not experience an emotional backlash if the ministry has been soundly based; Jesus is the same tomorrow, and the truth will still be true the morning after.

HEALING TOOLKIT

THE GIFT OF HEALING

A charismatic gift is literally a 'gift of grace'. It is not given *to* us but *through* us for the benefit of others (1 Corinthians 12:7). So when we pray for someone and they receive healing, this is a gift of healing given to that person through our moment of care and prayer. Such gifts may happen once, occasionally or regularly; that is God's decision. If it happens regularly, we may say someone 'has' a gift of healing.

God sometimes gives us one particular gift of healing. For example, we may be used to bring healing to people's wounded emotions, but not be so gifted when praying for those with persistent headaches. We need to be open to God to develop our gift of healing as He wills and guides.

Those with a regular gift of healing are called to serve the Church as a channel of the healing power of God. It is important to remember that such gifts are not meant to replace the healing ministry of the whole Church, but to resource the Church to fulfil that ministry.

It is misleading to talk about 'healers' in the Church; there is only one Healer, Jesus Christ. This distinguishes Christian healing from New Age and other healing approaches. Those who pray for healing are not authorities but fellow travellers. Healing is an activity of God. The intercessor and the supplicant pray – and wait.

PREPARATION

To make ourselves ready for involvement in the Church's healing ministry, we should:

- develop our relationship with God
- restore our relationships with others
- be more aware of our relationship with creation

THE WORD OF KNOWLEDGE

Jesus seemed to have just the right word to open people to their needs and the possibilities of change and healing. This is the purpose of the charismatic gift of the 'word of knowledge', which has been used by many people with a special gift of healing, famously by Kathryn Kuhlman. It is often used in large healing services where it is impossible to minister individually to everyone. The word of knowledge picks out those whom God is going to heal at this point.

An authentic gift like this is powerful and invaluable – and also unusual. Like all gifts it needs to be tested, and we need to question those who merely mimic it. We need to test the integrity of the person, and whether their words of knowledge are reliably true – a proven person and a proven ministry.

©istockphoto.com

PRAYING WITH FAITH

We live in a sceptical and critical society and we are all affected by this. In many ways it is a good thing because it helps us avoid a sense of magic and superstition. But it also makes it hard for us to approach praying for healing with a sense of anticipation. We are all too aware of the pitfalls.

Learning to pray with faith is more a 'letting go' than a 'grasping' – allowing our scepticism and questioning to slip away rather than trying to screw ourselves up into a frenzy of faith. This letting go is based on our conviction that in this situation we are right to trust in more than we can see.

As you look at the person before you, focus on the love, grace and power of God. The act of faith is to bring them together in your heart and mind, and thus be the 'link' between them and God. The challenge is to overcome our natural timidity and to approach God with expectancy, despite the obvious tension between their illness and the love of God for them.

USING YOUR WEAKNESS

We are often able to give to others what God has given to us. Indeed Paul tells us to draw on our own experience of difficulty, and turn it into help and comfort for others (2 Corinthians 1: 3-5).

So it should not seem strange that if we have received healing from depression, God may use us to bring healing to those who are also depressed.

LAYING ON HANDS

Our hands are our essential 'tools' in life, and probably the laying-on-of-hands is the oldest 'sacramental' action in human history. In the Old Testament it can mean many things, including:

- blessing (e.g. Genesis 48:15-16)
- commissioning (e.g. Numbers 27:18)
- healing (e.g. 2 Kings 4:34)

Jesus used touch to identify with sufferers such as lepers (Mark 1:41) as well as to heal, and the early church also used it for receiving the Holy Spirit (Acts 8;17, 19:6).

As well as its symbolic value, touch can convey love and acceptance in our prayers for healing, and can 'get through' to people very effectively. But like all body language, it is open to misunderstanding and even abuse, so it needs care and forethought. This is particularly true when praying for the young, or for someone of the opposite sex.

Laying on hands in prayer can be done on the head or shoulders, unless the person is suffering from headaches, head or neck injuries. This needs to be gentle, as the pressure of hands can feel heavy after a time. Some people place their hands *above* the person for this reason.

The troubled area of the body may also be touched, to convey care and the power to heal. This requires sensitivity, and it is best to ask the person to put your hand somewhere on their body if they would find that helpful. This helps them participate in their own healing and creates a greater sense of expectancy.

THE HEALING TOUCH

In almost half the recorded healing miracles in the gospels, it is specifically recorded that Jesus used touch of some sort. Touch was central in some healings. This practice was so well known that people begged Jesus to allow the sick to touch just the fringe of his cloak 'and all those who touched him were cured' (Mark 5:56). There was something powerfully 'sacramental' in the healing ministry of Jesus.

This is probably the origin of the early church practice of 'laying on of hands' for healing, as the early disciples imitated the practice of Jesus. Ananias laid hands on Paul after his Damascus Road experience, to that he would regain his sight (Acts 9:17). And Peter imitates both the hand gestures and the words of Jesus in raising Tabitha from death (Acts 9:40, compare Mark 5:41).

In the early church, the laying on of hands was accompanied by anointing with oil (James 5:14). Mark tells us that the disciples used oil on their first mission (Mark 6:13). Jesus may also have done so. On three occasions he used saliva, in a kind of anointing.

WHEN SOMETHING HAPPENS

It is important to be observant as we pray for people, and be prepared for things to happen:

Display of emotion

Often people can become overcome with tears and begin to shake during the prayers. Do not try to stop the flow of emotions, but it is best not to go on praying. However, maintain the laying on of hands if you are already doing this, as this conveys respect and support for what is happening. The giving of a tissue can also be a practical help – and an assurance of care.

As the emotion settles, it may help the process of prayer to ask the person, 'Would you like to share what is happening?' Depending on the answer (and whether they feel it appropriate to share anything), we can change our prayer focus accordingly. It may also help to invite the person to go somewhere more private if they wish to go on sharing.

Signs of disturbance

The person may become hostile or show signs of disturbance or psychological imbalance not in keeping with their normal conduct. This may be due to a variety of conditions; they may need some form of deliverance ministry, or the prayers may be aggravating a psychological condition. It is best to suspend the prayers and invite the person to explore what is happening confidentially.

This may be the time to recognise our limitations, and invite someone else with more expertise or knowledge to take over this part of the ministry. If we feel sure that there is spiritual interference, then we may conclude the time of prayer by taking authority in the name of Jesus and bind the hold of any spiritual powers from further activity. Include prayers of support and protection until the time of counsel or future prayer.

Resting in the Spirit

Sometimes when we pray with people, they are overcome by the touch of God and fall to the ground in an apparent faint. Do not be unduly worried about this, as the Bible contains a number of examples of people being overcome when they make connection with God – such as Daniel meeting Gabriel (Daniel 8:15-17), and John meeting the Son of Man (Revelation 1:13-18). In the healing ministry today, it is often also an expression of the release of tension, and an acceptance of the possibilities of God's healing power.

It is best to lower such people gently to the ground, make sure they are comfortable and in no distress, and simply to pray that God's touch continues to bring His healing to their lives. There is no need to pray in great detail at this point. Most people who have this experience report upon recovering that they felt a sense of intimacy with God when they were being reassured of His love and care for them. But it is not a guarantee of healing and should not be manipulated or even encouraged by those praying. For more on this experience, see Francis MacNutt's book *Overcome by the Spirit*.

WHEN NOTHING HAPPENS

Very often when we pray with others there is nothing discernable happening. In some ways this is the most challenging context of prayer for healing, and it is tempting to try and make something happen. Here we must trust that God is at work, even if we or the other person can see or feel nothing at the time.

Resist the urge to ask the person how they are feeling, as this can only lead to subjective conclusions on what has or has not been happening. We want the person to leave the time of prayer with their lives open to God and not dependent on us. It is best to have a short time of listening to God when you have finished your prayer, and then to take your hands off the person to indicate that the time of prayer is finished for this time. One of the important aspects of the work of prayer is to free the other person to take responsibility for their lives and to move on in their journey with God.

TESTS FOR TRUTH

As we evolve our theology of healing and embody it within the strategies and structures of church life, we shall find many problems and pitfalls. How can we check our progress? How can we know what is true and right?

As we consider any concept or proposed course of events, we must ask:

- Is this true to the teachings of the Bible *as a whole*?

- Is this true to what we know of Christ?

- Is this true to reason, as far as reason can take us?

- Is this true to experience – our experience and the experience of the Church throughout the ages?

- Is this true to the promptings of the Holy Spirit within us?

If an idea is false it will founder on one or more of these tests. They are spotlights on God's truth; we need to be sure they are all shining.

We will probably need help as we sift and sort ideas in this way. Most denominations have national and regional advisers in the healing ministry. See below for a list of helpful organisations.

CONTACTS

- **The Acorn Christian Healing Foundation**
  (Rev Dr Russ Parker),
  Whitehill Chase, High Street
  Bordon, Hants GU35 0AP
  01420 478121
  www.acornchristian.org

- **The Guild of Health (Revd Roger Hoath)**
  St Marylebone Church
  17 Marylebone Road, London NW1 5LT
  020 7563 1389
  www.gohealth.org.uk

- **The Guild of St Raphael** (Revd Dr Paul Nener)
  St John's Vicarage, Green Lane, Stoneycroft
  Liverpool L13 7EA
  0151 228 2023

- **The Order of St Luke** (Revd Bob Ash)
  28 Woodlands Farm Road
  Erdington, Birmingham B24 0PG
  0121 351 1529

- **Green Pastures Christian Centre of Healing**
  17 Burton Road
  Branksome Park, Poole, Dorset BH13 6DT
  01202 764776
  www.green-pastures.org

- **Harnhill Centre of Christian Healing**
  (Revd Paul & Mrs Bryony Springate)
  Harnhill Manor, Cirencester, Glocs GL7 5PX
  01285 850283
  www.harnhillcentre.org.uk

- **Burrswood Christian Centre (Dr Gareth Tuckwell)**
  Groombridge, Tunbridge Wells, Kent TN3 9PY
  01892 896 637
  www.burrswood.org.uk

- **Christian Healing Mission (Revd John Ryeland)**
  8 Cambridge Court,, 210 Shepherds Bush Road
  London W6 7NJ
  020 7603 8118
  www.healingmission.org

- **Breath Ministries
  (Revd John & Mrs Christine Huggett)**
  10a High Street. Tunbridge Wells TN1 1UX
  01892 514112

- **Crowhurst Christian Healing Centre
  Revd Kath Batte**
  The Old Rectory, Crowhurst, Battle TN33 9AD
  01424 830204
  www.crowhursthealing.co.uk

- **Baptist Union Health & Healing Fellowship**
  (Revd Elsie Howell)
  60 Andrew Allen Road
  Rockwell Green, Wellington TA21 9DY
  01823 664529

- **URC/Methodist Health & Healing Development Group** (Revd Jim Needham)
  15 The Old Nurseries, Grange over Sands LL11 7AD
  01539 532050

- **URC/Methodist Health & Healing Development Group** (Revd Delia Bond)
  URC Church House, 86 Tavistock Place
  London WC1H 9RT
  020 7916 2020
  www.urc.org.uk

CHANNELS OF HEALING

Anything which helps us discern and practise the presence of Jesus will become for us a channel of Christian healing. The classical channels are:

- **prayer**: 'Prayer offered in faith will make the sick person well' (James 5:15).
- **laying on of hands**: Paul did this right up the end of his ministry (Acts 28:8-9).
- **preaching the gospel**: God confirms the message with remarkable healings (such as Acts 14:3).

- **deliverance**: a standard part of the ministry of Jesus (such as Mark 1:34). Human beings can be damaged by the world, the flesh or the devil, but God's love brings healing to them all.
- **anointing**: a practice begun by the disciples during Jesus' lifetime (Mark 6:12-13). Usually reserved for special need or more acute or serious conditions.
- **confession**: this is sometimes the gateway to healing (James 5:16).
- **listening**: at the age of 12 Jesus knew how to listen and ask questions (Luke 3:46), and this characterised his healing ministry. It is a healing quality; 'everyone should be quick to listen, slow to speak' (James 1:19).
- **practical acts of love**: prayer is not a substitute for action.

But anything which helps us practise the presence of Jesus can be a channel of healing.

So in Acts 19:11-12, when Paul's healing ministry was perhaps much in demand and he could not personally visit all those who needed him, he sent used handkerchiefs and aprons to the sick and these become channels of healing. It was not that they had magic properties, but they brought the presence of Paul to them, and Paul brought the presence of Jesus, and Jesus made a difference to their lives.

Church life should consist of countless such channels of healing. Here are a few:

- **funeral ministry**: helping mourners to affirm the deceased, to be set free from a sense of hurt, and to discover the risen Christ.
- **marriage preparation**: 'preventative medicine' against the 'sicknesses' which often afflict marriages in our society.
- **all-age worship**: honouring the place of the young, and healing the generation gap.
- **community programmes**: care for the elderly, the young, groups with special problems, campaigns to address local issues. The healing power of Jesus is not just heavenly minded; it is of earthly use.
- **parish social activities**: such as Harvest Suppers and parish holidays, healing the gap between young and old.
- **baptism and confirmation preparation**: presenting the reality and relevance of Jesus and inviting a response.
- **festivals**: imaginative services and activities for public occasions, perhaps including a healing moment. What about Remembrance Sunday?
- **visiting**: balanced so that contact, comfort and challenge are all offered.
- **teaching**: treatment of life-centred topics, applying the Bible to areas of life which need Christ's healing touch.
- **quiet days**: times of silence together in which to listen to God.

The Church Council should also be a channel of healing. Some people dread Council meetings as chores at best and occasions for conflict at worst. But beginning with prayer and some Bible study can set the tone for the whole meeting.

The Council has an important role in reviewing church life and policy, and can ask the question 'What would Jesus do?' This is a healing question because it places his purposes above our preferences.

Occasionally the question can be put in the negative form: what do we presently do which is irrelevant to God's healing purposes? We should then ask whether this has any place in the church programme at all.

FURTHER READING

See *Healing and Evangelism* by Russ Parker and Roy Lawrence (Triangle 1996) for more suggestions about how to build healing moments into church and civic services.

WORKING IN THE OVERLAP

PURPOSE

This Unit helps you reflect on what is involved in working with ill people in the church and the health-care settings, and guides you in making appropriate choices for yourself in whether you are called to work with the sick, and how.

CONTENTS

Using the bridge   84
Which community?   86
The survival of the fit   88

USING THE BRIDGE

COMPETENCE ZONE

We live in an age of specialisms. Each one of us knows more and more – about less and less. Nowhere is this more true than in the field of science and health. The hospital has its many specialists and departments, each being careful to observe the boundaries between their competence and that of others. The Church too is increasingly aware of issues of competence, with training courses for many of the roles played in local churches and rules about who is allowed to do what (like help on the healing team).

In many ways all this is a good thing. The specialist treatment of many diseases could not happen without it. Specialisation narrows down our viewpoint so that we concentrate on the specific problem facing us, until we find a solution. It's the view down the microscope – through specialisation we now see detail undreamt of 100 years ago. The result is that (in the Western world at least) we enjoy a degree of health and welfare never before experienced by whole societies in the history of humanity.

But with this specialisation has come a strong and exclusive sense of 'competence'. If you don't have this particular specialist knowledge or ability, then you shouldn't try to help with this particular problem. You need to leave it to the experts, those who 'know' – about this.

The down-side of specialisation is that the 'experts' do not focus on the wider picture. And the truth is that no situation in life is 'narrow'; it is complex and has many facets. So experts need to work in the 'overlap' – alongside other experts, and alongside non-specialists who try to keep the wider picture in view.

> **A problem-centred approach assumes there is a solution, but Christian faith invites us further and further into the mystery.**
> *A Time to Heal* page 128

COMFORT ZONE

The narrowing of our view can also turn into the narrowing of our attitudes. It is comfortable to work within the area of our competence, with other people who share the same viewpoint. We have so much in common, and we get on so well.

So the hospital can become a separate 'zone', staffed by people who all see things in much the same way. Chaplains and Visitors work within the system very much on the hospital's terms. There is a crisp dividing line between their work and the activities of the wider Church – whose practices in Christian healing may be kept at a distance. They are too uncomfortable. They may question the all-embracing competence of the medical profession to bring health and healing to those who suffer.

Equally the Church is often inward-looking, and resists the hard questions posed to its healing ministry by the medical profession. Perhaps the hospital has been too successful – too good at doing the healing that Jesus was famous for, but which the Church now largely fails to do. So as it tries to recapture its healing ministry, it may distance itself from its 'rival' and seek ways of healing that ignore the insights and skills of modern medicine. We do healing 'our way' – even 'God's way'.

But such separation is unhelpful, and again the call is to work in the overlap – and to become comfortable in zones other than our 'own'.

©istockphoto.com/dawn liljenquist

CROSSING OVER

If we want to avoid getting tied up in our own little 'zone' and we want to keep the wider picture in view, here are some things that may help:

- **Get to know** what happens on the other side of the divide. If you have never been to a healing service in a church before, find one and go. In particular, find one you think you are not going to 'like', one that will question much of what you believe about health and healing. You will always learn *something*.

  Equally, if you have never talked to a hospital Chaplain (and especially if you have never been in hospital at all), go and find one. Ask if you might accompany an experienced Visitor for an afternoon, to get a feel for the hospital environment. You are not likely to meet a more committed group of people.

- **Learn to respect** the sincere work of others, and their desire to bring the grace of God to those who are ill. The treatment for this particular illness may be obvious and well-established; but it is not the person's only need, and perhaps (from God's point of view) not their greatest. So they may indeed need prayer.

Equally, perhaps this ill person ought to look to God for the fulfilment of their needs as a whole person; but if we have a way of easing this condition, won't God respect the human love and dedication that has gone into developing that treatment?

- **Keep involved in both** aspects of healing. If your ministry is in the hospital setting (in whatever kind of role), keep a small involvement in a church-based healing ministry. If your ministry lies in praying for others as part of a healing team in church, arrange some involvement in a health-care setting. Push the book trolley around the local hospice – anything to keep you in touch with the disciplined exercise of medical skills.

  This twin involvement will enable you to be citizens of two zones. And when someone you care for and pray for needs to cross from one zone to the other, you can be their confident guide.

- **Beware of prejudice**. It's not a nice word, but it's sometimes true. If we are defensive and suspicious about what goes on on the other side of the divide, what is this based on? If we can't explain it clearly, then it may simply be prejudice – a strong but unexamined negative feeling. We need to be open to healing in many forms – not just as we know it ourselves.

MANY-SIDED

People's lives can develop fully only through the harmonious evolution of a fourfold relationship:

to the good earth beneath our feet, our physical environment	to other people, to our living and human environment
to ourselves, through a right ordering of our own inner and complex existence	to God, the source of all our being

Adapted from Stephen Neill. So healing will require a large team of resources: environmentalists, priests, psychologists, sociologists, doctors, alternative medicine practitioners, town planners, architects, peace-makers, politicians. No one of these can cover the whole agenda of health.

WHICH COMMUNITY?

A community is a grouping of people held together by – something. That something can be a wide range of things, from blood-ties to culture to religion to common goals. In earlier ages people tended to belong to just one community, and within it they would live, do their work, marry and have children, and eventually die. Today we tend to belong to several communities at the same time. We will even be a somewhat different person in one community setting than we are within another.

The **Church** is such a community. Christians are drawn into a common life together because of their shared faith in Christ and their shared task of working out God's kingdom purposes in the world. This is the community context within which we often find our basic sense of identity as Christians – as God's children, as saved and redeemed people, as a priesthood to the world. We can minister to people who are ill from within that community context.

The **hospital** is another such community. It also has a common life and norms that govern it, and the community shares in the task of caring for and curing those who are ill. It is dedicated to developing our God-given wisdom and understanding to meet the needs of those who suffer, within clear and professional guidelines. Christians can minister to people who are ill from within this community context as well.

CHOOSE YOUR COMMUNITY

We get into trouble when we 'mix' our communities. Our workplace community will have different norms and expectations from those we have at home; we will relate differently to people as a result. What you do and say at the pub or at a football match cannot necessarily be transferred to the church prayer meeting or the school parents' evening. We need to act appropriately for our different 'belongings' in life.

If your gift is to serve those who are ill, you need to know how to do this appropriately within either the church or the health-care setting. Probably it will be primarily one or the other, and you need to choose where you 'belong'.

The choice is similar to that faced by Christians who feel called to teach the Christian faith to children.

- Do they train as RE teachers and work within the school setting, with all its opportunities but also its professional limitations?

- Or do they train as Sunday school teachers and work in the church setting, with only those children who come to church but with greater freedom to teach and model the Christian faith?

The opportunities are different. Each has its norms and expectations. Whatever you choose, you need to feel settled that this is the context that matches your gifts and your calling.

The **hospital** will bring you into contact with a wide spectrum of society, including those very negative about the church. But no-one comes into hospital to see the Chaplain, and they have not asked for their wider spiritual needs to be addressed. They are also a captive audience, and you need to be sensitive about this.

The **church** setting is composed of people who have all chosen to be here, and want God to minister to them – especially if they come forward for prayer. They may have an uncomfortable level of faith that God is going to work wonders. But what about all those who would never step inside a church building?

Both of these settings require considerable devotion and the exercise of faith. You need to discern where your primary calling lies.

SHOULD FLORENCE PRAY?

In October 2000 a nurse was found guilty of serious professional misconduct for attempting to exorcise evils spirits from a patient. She considered that it was part of the nurse's role to pray with the patient if they requested it and agreed to it. But she was regarded as having stepped over the line, and to have allowed her religious practices to displace her professional ones.

Where do your sympathies lie here - and does that help you to know which 'community' you feel you can belong to?

Some of that may be discerning the 'spiritual' from the 'religious'. Do we want to help ordinary people towards a deeper meaning in life and re-awakening their sense of the spiritual; or do we want to help those who already have some faith to reach out and grasp all that God has for them? Where does your heart lie?

THE SURVIVAL OF THE FIT

Working with those who are ill, in the name of Christ, is a demanding calling. If you want to survive, you need to make your gifts and characteristics fit the role, and fit the setting you will work within.

Mark yourself out of 5 for each of the following statements, laid out in four groups of six.

    5 = unusually gifted in this
    4 = one of my stronger points
    3 = competent enough
    2 = one of my weaker points
    1 = forget it!

☐ 1. I am good at listening.

☐ 2. I enjoy explaining things to others from the Bible.

☐ 3. I am often used to bring others to Christ.

☐ 4. I feel a deep, caring love for those who are ill, and want to help them get well.

☐ 5. I like making or designing things.

☐ 6. I am deeply concerned about the world's problems and people in need.

☐ 1. I make helpful relationships with others easily.

☐ 2. Others are helped when I teach them things about Jesus and Christian living.

☐ 3. God has given me great love for others and a longing to win them for Him.

☐ 4. Others find my presence soothing and healing.

☐ 5. I like helping other people.

☐ 6. I am active in service in the community.

Here is an exercise to help you weight that up. Match yourself to the statements below, and score yourself. Then write some reflections, bearing in mind all you have read in this workbook so far.

☐ 1. Others seem to find me encouraging and share their problems with me.

☐ 2. I love study and finding the facts.

☐ 3. I find my life is full of opportunities to witness for Christ.

☐ 4. I have sometimes given advice to the sick and they have been helped.

☐ 5. I am a practical type, good at do-it-yourself jobs and making use of odds and ends.

☐ 6. I am very aware of people who are deprived today, and feel I should do something about them.

☐ 1. I really care about other people.

☐ 2. I have patience in helping others understand Christian things; it seems so worthwhile.

☐ 3. I love to talk to others about Jesus.

☐ 4. I spend time praying with and for sick people.

☐ 5. I spend a lot of time helping others in practical ways.

☐ 6. Social and political issues seem to me to be crying out for Christian witness and involvement.

Then look at the guidance opposite and work out your scores for relevant giftings for:

- Care for the sick generally ☐
- A healing ministry in the church context ☐
- Care for the ill in the health-care context ☐

Adapted from an original survey by Lewis Misselbrook

My strengths for the health-care situation

My strengths for the church situation

My strengths for both situations equally

Add together your scores for all questions 1 and 4, and put these in the 'care for the sick' box.

Add together your scores for all questions 2 and 3, and put these in the 'church context' box.

Add together your scores for all questions 5 and 6, and put these in the 'health care context' box.

My weaknesses in the health-care situation

My weaknesses in the church situation

My conclusions

HARD
QUESTIONS

PURPOSE

This Unit deals with many of the difficult questions and problematic situations that arise when we serve those who are ill in Christ's name. It is important to address these issues, while not allowing them to drive our policy and practice.

CONTENTS

Why weren't they healed?	92
How does faith work?	94
Why is God so unfair?	96
More harm than good?	98
All in the mind?	100
Differently abled?	101
How can I cope with failure?	102
Medical confirmation?	103
Living with questions	104

WHY WEREN'T THEY HEALED?

God is a mystery and will always remain so. The temptation to satisfy our understanding of His ways in healing can have the same delicious aroma as the original 'apple' tree in the Garden of Eden. We want to know everything.

In the last analysis, our duty is to walk humbly with our God, listening to the promptings of His Spirit as we pray for those of His children who are hurting. We need to learn to leave the outcome of our prayers to the higher wisdom of our Lord.

But within that humility, we can look to the ministry of Jesus for some pointers:

- Even Jesus did not heal everyone. Some gospel stories record that he healed every kind of disease and on occasions healed everyone who came to him (e.g. Matthew 4:23-24). But on other occasions he seems to have healed just one person (e.g. by the pool of Bethesda, John 5:3-6), leaving the others untouched.

- Jesus did not have a standard pattern for his healing ministry. He varied it, perhaps appropriately to each situation. If we approach all ill people in exactly the same way, perhaps we do not understand each situation as we should.

- Even at Jesus' hands, the blind man at Bethsaida (Mark 8:22-26) needed to be prayed for twice before he saw people clearly. There will be people for whom we have to pray in faith several times before anything changes.

Other considerations may also help us to keep a 'failure' to heal in perspective:

- God may be releasing the naturally created healing mechanisms of the body to do their normal job over time. He may be repositioning an unstable memory deep in the psyche, an alteration that may take years to bear fruit. God has His own timetable. The fact that there is no immediate visible change does not mean that no change has taken place.

- Deuteronomy 28 includes serious illnesses in the list of consequences of sin and unfaithfulness to God (verses 21-22, 28, 35, 59-61). St Paul links illness and death with having taken Holy Communion unworthily (1 Corinthians 11:27-30). If serious sin is one of the causes of an illness, then repentance, forgiveness and restoration will be central and essential elements in seeking healing from God.

- God loves to surprise us. Most of those Jesus healed had no previous relationship with him. Today God's healing touch on individuals is often part of his 'courtship of love', before his Lordship is acknowledged.

- God is not a system. While some may be praying with great faith and see little change, others who have strayed from God in their personal lives continue to be used by God to heal others. We may not understand this, but we must respect His choices.

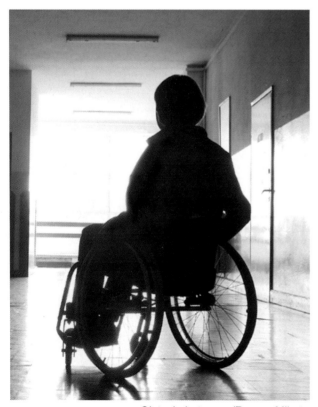

©istockphoto.com/Roman Milert

● A healing miracle fades into insignificance in comparison with a fresh revelation of God's love for an individual. Sometimes this, and not a healing, is the result of our prayers.

WILLING TO BE WELL?

Every GP and priest can recall people who make numerous visits for help, but their situation seems impossible to solve. We must consider whether this person really wants to get better.

● An unwanted child in a dysfunctional family may grow up with a deeply-buried belief that the only way to get attention or achieve significance is by being ill.

● A mother may repeatedly present her child to a doctor – not as an independent human being but as a pathological object that embodies her own illness. The child finds that any attempt to break out of this 'ill role' provokes another outpouring of smothering behaviour by the mother.

No wonder that in later life, such people have a very ambivalent attitude to illness and to seeking and accepting healing. They may be desperate to escape from the prison, but at the same time have a phobia of freedom – it is fearful, unknown territory, bringing back memories of a painful childhood. The pain of rejection finds consolation in the repeated attention of carers acting as substitute parent figures. Illness becomes a respectable ticket for the love for which an empty heart craves.

Thus there are significant advantages in remaining ill: it avoids the phobia, attracts kindly attention, and avoids the daily responsibilities required of those who are strong and independent. They truly do not want to be well. Their path to healing must first negotiate this issue.

---

11 REASONS WHY PEOPLE ARE NOT HEALED

Francis MacNutt offers eleven reasons why in his experience people are not healed when they are prayed for (*Healing*, Ave Maria Press 1974).

Our lack of faith
Those who pray for healing have not developed enough faith, just as Jesus' disciples had not (Matthew 17:14-20).

Redemptive suffering
At times, God uses sickness for the better purpose of bringing salvation to others. So Paul's illness was instrumental in bringing others to faith (Galatians 4:13-14).

False value on suffering
People may believe that God has somehow sent the suffering, so there is a strong subconscious resistance to healing.

Sin
The illness may be linked to resentment, undue anger or refusal to forgive.

Not praying specifically
Failure to discern the exact root cause of the problem. Sometimes this needs to be discovered specifically, especially in prayer for inner healing.

Faulty diagnosis
Such as praying for physical healing, when inner healing was the basic need.

Rejection of medicine
The person is refusing to use the normal means of seeking healing, preferring to ask for a supernatural solution.

Neglect of health
The person is not taking proper care of their body and of their personal life, such as unwise diet, worry or overwork.

Now is not the time
God's timing is not ours. We prefer instant healing; often there is a delay, or healing takes place gradually.

A different instrument
Perhaps I am not the person who has the discernment to pray for this particular person.

Poor social environment
Some healing will not take place until our relationships and our society are healed. We need Christian communities where people can be loved into wholeness.

HOW DOES FAITH WORK?

Looking to God for healing requires the exercise of faith. But what kind of faith? And how much of it? And why does such faith so often elude us?

WHAT FAITH IS

Christian faith is a form of personal trust. Since God is a person (or rather a Trinity of persons), then faith in God is trusting that Person to be faithful to whatever He has promised. Faith is a relationship that is living, dynamic and two-way (think of the faith God keeps putting in *us* in the ministry of healing!). We need to be suspicious of definitions of faith which stray away from the concept of personal trust.

> **The gift of healing is not given to the one who prays, but to the one who gets better.**

Faith is 'being sure of what we hope for and certain of what we do not see' (Hebrews 11:1). It is a sense of confidence in God, no matter what happens. Hebrews 11 is full of stories of people who were convinced that God was working His purposes out in them. Some conquered against all the odds. Others suffered terribly and apparently did not overcome (see verses 35-38). All these had faith – and all these Old Testament believers died believing that there was more to God's promises than they had so far received (verse 13).

GILDING THE LILY

Some fall into the temptation to exaggerate the fruit of the healing ministry. This is a sign of immaturity. Such a person is not resting on God's love, but seeking to gain security and attention by being associated with remarkable events.

The outcome of healing prayer should, from a personal perspective, be almost irrelevant to the one who prays. Their duty is to obey the call to intercede. God takes the responsibility for the answer, and the recipient receives the answer with gratitude. The intercessor's only pleasure should be in witnessing his friend's blessing. That witness can later bless others, in a calm and steady testimony. Any exaggeration builds a card house of false faith on a sandy foundation.

But alongside our personal faith in God there is also the 'gift of faith' (1 Corinthians 12:8-9). Like all gifts of the Spirit, not all Christians have this gift – just as not all Christians have the gift of healing.

- If we do not have this gift, we may pray for it but we cannot 'claim' it.
- If we have it – even if it is still rather latent and under-developed – it will grow with use.

We may need the help and discernment of others to know which is the case.

FAITH – FOR WHAT?

Jesus healed ten people of their leprosy (Luke 17:11-18). But one came back to give thanks to the Lord, and he was made 'completely well'.

The woman with internal bleeding (Luke 8:42-48) was cured as she touched the edge of Jesus' clothing, unnoticed by everyone else. Jesus drew her out to give public testimony to her faith – and her faith brought her 'salvation', complete health.

These distinctions are brought out in the Greek words used in the gospels:

- ***iomai*** and ***therapeuo*** describe physical healing
- ***sodzo*** means 'heal' in the wider sense, and is also the usual NT word for 'save'

In Jesus' ministry, physical healing was not a special blessing reserved for those who were particularly deserving or who showed exceptional faith. Many were healed and apparently did not go on to experience that wider salvation that Jesus came to bring.

Jesus never asked a person whether they had enough faith to be healed before he healed them. But he often asked the question, 'What do you want me to do for you?' When the person told Jesus what they wanted, he called this faith. Rather than indulge in introspective reflections on whether we or the other person has enough faith before we pray, we should seek to give the person room to tell us what they want of God. In response, like Jesus, we are to respect their request and pray for it with all our hearts.

GREAT FAITH

It is true that Jesus chided his disciples for having 'little faith' (Matthew 6:30, 8:26, 14:31, 16:8, 17:20), and commended 'great faith' (Matthew 8:10, 15:28). But faith is not a quantifiable substance that fills our spirit like a storage tank. It cannot be earned or stored up in advance like a spiritual bank account. We cannot measure the level to check that we have enough stored up to pay for a particularly challenging prayer request.

We should think of 'faith for healing' more as:

- an awareness of the nature of the Father's loving heart
- a discernment of His particular purposes for a hurting person
- the courage to pray in the light of both those things.

FAITH IS

- **in God's power — He can heal.**
- **in God's love — He wants to heal.**
- **in God's wisdom — He might not heal.**

So faith in the context of prayer for healing has three aspects.

- our ongoing relationship and trust in God.
- a gift of discernment or knowledge, such that we see the situation as God sees it.
- a special confidence that is given as a gift of the Spirit for a particular request at a particular time.

If we do not have confidence that someone is going to be healed, it is important to consider where that lack of confidence comes from. It may lie in any one of these three aspects, and the remedy for each is very different.

> *My faith is not in my faith, but in God.*
> **Francis MacNutt**

We must be careful in accusing ourselves – or others – of having little faith. We cannot earn or deserve the power to heal. But we can learn to trust God more, and we can become wiser in our discernment of God's purposes. These two together are the basis for the exercise of 'great faith'.

We must also recognise that great things sometimes happen even through 'little faith'. Even faith as small as a grain of mustard seed can achieve great things (Matthew 17:20). And God is not restricted by a lack of discernment: a trusting child pleading for his friend can bring the healing touch of God as much as a mature adult who is wise and experienced in matters of faith.

NOTES

WHY IS GOD SO UNFAIR?

'We know that all things work together for good to them that love God.'

This Authorised Version text of Romans 8:28 is precious to many Christians, and can bring comfort and solace to people going through difficult times. Perhaps every single thing that happens in the world, no matter how bad, is really working out some good purpose of God – if only we have the faith to see it.

The problem is that this does not seem true to human experience. Within the structure of the Universe, things do not automatically work out satisfactorily.

- Three out of four children born each day die of malnutrition or become chronic invalids because they are undernourished.

- Christians continue to be persecuted for their faith, sometimes suffering terribly.

- A young woman stands widowed and childless, her husband the victim of a bombing incident, her 2-year old gunned down by a rival faction.

Have all things worked together for good for these people who have loved God as best they could? Some people give up religion because they discover in the crucible of human experience that life does not automatically turn out well.

The AV translation of Paul's words captures a certain attitude to life, but is not true to Paul's original words or his own attitude to life. He did not believe in the Universe as an orderly system which will all come right in the end. Hope for the future is not embedded in the structure of creation but depends on the acts of God. Paul's gospel is not one of happy coincidences – he preached a God who has acted to save a fallen world and who calls us now to work with Him to further his good purposes.

WHAT IS GOOD?

Some modern translations offer us another perspective:

In everything God works for good with those who love him. (RSV)

In everything God cooperates for good with those who love Him. (NEB)

Paul is not claiming that calamity is good, or will come right in the end. He is not an 'evolutionary optimist'. But he is convinced that the God who raised Jesus Christ from the dead is not to be defeated by any set of circumstances that may confront us. He looked for – and found – God's cooperation in working out good purposes in the world, even in the most calamitous situations.

If we think that God will work in our lives to keep us safe from all harm and give us all we desire, then at some point in our lives we are going to be disappointed. Prayer is not a 'magic' formula through which we can manipulate our own ends. (That is the essence of magic – which is why it is condemned throughout Scripture.) Prayer is asking for the goodness of God to be worked out in our lives and in the lives of others.

So what is God's goodness? It is that we should all become sons and daughters of God and be conformed to the image of Christ. That is God's good purpose, and everything else needs to be judged in the light of it. This stands in contrast to a world that sees happiness and comfort as the ultimate purpose of life.

GOOD FOR WHAT?

The question then is whether this world, with all its disease and suffering, is a good place for the working out of the good purposes of God. There are several aspects of this:

- God created a good world on two principles: a physical world that runs on consistent natural laws, and an element of human freedom. This was a good context for the emergence of good 'people' who would be like Himself.

- When evil entered God's good creation, there was a massive disruption of creation. God is not pleased with the present state of affairs on the Planet either.

- It was humanity that let that evil in; and creation waits for the full redemption of humanity for its own healing (see Romans 8:19-22). So resolving our own sinfulness is the key to solving all the other problems that now exist in the world.

- God has not caused the present state of affairs, but He allows it to continue – because it is a good context in which human beings can be redeemed and transformed. It is 'good for His good purposes'.

The distinction between what God *causes* and what God *allows* is important. Giving your daughter a pair of ice skates knowing she may fall over on them, is very different from knocking her down on the ice. If God wants a world which runs according to consistent laws and is populated by free human beings, he cannot also go around making sure everyone is protected from every kind of harm.

A PLACE FOR SUFFERING

C S Lewis said that God whispers to us in our pleasures, speaks in our conscience, but shouts in our pain. He called pain 'the megaphone of God' to rouse a dead world. The existence of suffering in our world is a scream to all of us that something is wrong. It halts us in our tracks and forces us to consider other values. Some other religious systems try to deny pain or encourage people to rise above it. Christianity asserts that suffering exists – as proof of a fallen world. This vision of a 'great but fallen world' matches our day to day experience. It fits the double nature of our world – and of ourselves.

Imagine the Intensive Care ward of a hospital. All sorts of people pace the lobby – rich, poor, black, white, clever, dull, of various religions and none. But none of these divisions make a scrap of difference; all are united in the face of the illness and possible death of a relative or friend. They are facing life at its most essential. Some call for a chaplain or priest for the first time in their lives, and ponder ultimate questions of life, death and meaning.

Often we want to look backwards to find out 'why?'. God encourages us to look *forward* – to answer the same question. In the Bible the problem of pain is not addressed as a philosophical riddle but as a test of human response and faithfulness. God never explained the origin of Job's suffering; the question was what Job would do in the midst of tragedy. The emphasis is on our response. The 'why' is found in the good that can be drawn out of suffering – if we will cooperate with God as He cooperates with us.

Things did not always work out the way Jesus wanted them to. He foresaw his own death, but he did not want it, as he said clearly to his Father in Gethsemane. But he had confidence that God would bring good out of that horrible situation – and he was spectacularly right.

Our True Friend in life is not the Universe, not Mother Nature, not Lady Luck, but the Creator God. If we believe in 'friendly nature', we are going to be shocked by the way things are. But people can look for the active help of a personal God when things become unfriendly. The promise here is absolute: if we love God and want His will, then He is working with us to bring good out of even very difficult circumstances.

Pain and trouble and trials and sorrows ... to all who love God they are tokens from him. To all who do not love God they are a nuisance.
Dr Edward Wilson who accompanied Captain Scott to the Antarctic

MORE HARM THAN GOOD?

One of the most stinging criticisms made of the Christian healing ministry is that some people are in a worse state after it than they were before. Where this is true, it is extremely serious – it can (quite properly) lead to legal action against the Church, and all the good work done in bringing health and healing in Christ's name is brought into disrepute.

The 'more harm than good' possibility is one that Jesus himself flagged up in relation to deliverance (Luke 11:24-26), and we need good practice ourselves and good advice for those who ask for prayer, if we are to avoid it.

NO MORE MEDICINES

Some of those who come for prayer may be taking medication. It is stupid and harmful to tell such people to give up their medicine now that they have come for prayer and healing in the name of Jesus. Jesus counselled the ten lepers who came to him for healing to go and visit the health authorities of his day – the priests in Jerusalem. It was as they took this advice that they were miraculously healed (Luke 17:14).

A healing service in church should not become an opportunity to be dismissive or disparaging of medicine. Many members of church prayer teams are GPs and nurses. Our role is to pray with people, accepting all the other measures they are taking in relation to their health. This is even true of their recourse to various alternative therapies, unless an explicit conflict arises between Christian faith and the 'spirituality' of the alternative approach.

FALSE HOPE

It is tempting to encourage those who suffer and assure them that they are going to get better. We believe in the love and care of God, and in His power to heal; and we find it hard to live with the disappointment (theirs and ours) should it not happen.

Too many times people have been sent away having been told that they will surely be cured. We cause such people further pain and heartache if they are not healed in response to our confidence.

We could learn good lessons from doctors and nurses who are often asked, 'Am I going to get better?' A good reply will not crush their faith or give them false hope. We might say, 'This is my hope for you, and for this I am praying with all my heart.' Such sentiments can encourage hope and trust, while not promising things that are not ours to give.

The exception is when we have been given a prophetic insight from God that a person will get better. This needs testing quite rigorously with other Christian people, especially church leaders, before acting on it. We need to weigh up the damage that will be caused if we are wrong.

BLAMING THE SICK

It is hard for us when our prayers are not answered in the way we had confidence they would be. This can be an unnerving and vulnerable moment for us. The temptation is to look for reasons in the sick person, rather than leaving the mystery with God.

It is common to accuse the sick person of not having enough faith – which is seldom the case. It is better to ask whether we might need to deepen our faith through spending more time in the presence of God. We may need to come to the place where we are more sure that God is with us and for us, than whether He is going to use us or not. At the best of times, suffering and healing is a mystery, and we have to learn to live with this.

RESORT TO THE DEMONIC

If a person is not healed, we can begin to hunt obsessively for a reason! With the revival of interest in spiritual warfare and the demonic, some people have been told that the reason they are not healed is because they have a demon within them. This can be dangerous and harmful, and is usually untrue. It is best to trust God to go on touching the person's life and leave the matter there, unless we have actual evidence of their involvement in the occult or similar activities.

©istockphoto.com/mustafa deliormanli

CHARTER FOR HEALING

A Charter for Healing was written by Roy McCloughry and Michèle Taylor as part of the Disability and Theology Research Project at Kingdom Trust. The following excerpts are especially relevant here:

- Every person who asks for prayer for healing should be treated with respect and dignity. They should not be embarrassed or exploited nor should their wishes be ignored. This is particularly important when the ministry of healing takes place publicly.

- If an intercessor uses a particular symbol in prayer (such as laying on of hands or anointing with oil) the significance of this should be explained to the supplicant and their consent obtained. The supplicant should, at any point, have the freedom to stop whatever is going on.

- No pressure should be put on a supplicant, by any means, to state that they have been healed. They should feel that they have the freedom to say that they do not think they are, to the best of their knowledge. Neither should pressure be put on them to say that they feel any changes in their body (such as heat or pins and needles) unless they do so freely and of their own volition.

- Healing is not a matter of success or failure. Praying for somebody shows that they are cared for and included in the family of God, and shows solidarity with them. Neither those who pray, nor those prayed for, should carry this additional burden.

- Where testimony is given, the supplicant should be able to deliver their testimony in their own words, from their perspective. No pressure should be brought to bear on them, and neither should testimony be given on their behalf, either in spoken or written form, without their consent.

- Prayer for healing does not complete the church's responsibility. It may be important to refer people for continuing pastoral care. Offering prayer for healing means that we are willing to follow up people, ensuring that the church expresses continuity of appropriate care.

- Where someone comes for healing prayer with an overt impairment it should not be assumed that they have come for prayer for that impairment. The supplicant may not perceive their impairment to be a problem which needs healing. There is no substitute for careful listening.

- It may be extremely harmful to be told that one is not healed because of sin (either one's own or that of previous generations), or because of lack of faith. In the majority of instances the person who is praying for healing cannot know that this is true. It may be true that a person is struggling morally or with their faith. Such a person needs support, encouragement and care rather than accusation. Any problems should be dealt with privately in the context of pastoral care.

- People who pray for healing need pastoral care and accountability if they are to exercise their ministry with confidence and integrity. They may also face situations which drain them physically, emotionally and spiritually, and need places of retreat where they can find refreshment and new energy for their ministry.

ALL IN THE MIND?

Physical symptoms sometimes arise from subconscious stress or other disorders of the emotions. Generally we call these physical ailments 'psychosomatic' – the person's 'psyche' or inner person is affecting their 'soma' or body.

People who are sceptical about prayer for healing often take the view that whenever a 'healing' takes place in response to prayer, the physical symptoms were in fact psychosomatic. The prayer affected their inner person and brought a greater measure of health there; as a result, the physical symptoms also disappeared. This view is all too often driven by a belief that God does not intervene in the physical world – or of course that God does not exist at all.

It is beyond dispute that some physical disorders are psychosomatic, and that healing of these disorders through prayer does indeed often work through the healing of the inner person. But these disorders are no less genuine or painful – certainly no guilt attaches to having them – and their healing is significant.

Within medicine, these disorders are known as 'hysterical', although different from the everyday meaning of the word. 'Hysterical' comes from the Greek *uteros* meaning a womb, and implies that the symptoms arise from the very womb or centre of someone's being, deeper than and beyond the control of the conscious mind. They are not fraudulent symptoms, even though they may be a way of escape from intolerable stress.

NO DIVISIONS

God sees each sufferer as a whole person, not divided into physical and emotional subsections. When as a result of prayer a person with a psychosomatic condition is relieved of their suffering, this in no way lessens the value of the healing for the sufferer, nor does it disprove the reality of the Father's care.

We should not divide the person either. Every turning of the human heart towards God and the receiving of His love to transform their inner person, is a miracle of God's grace. It is no less so for being hidden from view. Regardless of the origin of a symptom, either physical or unconscious, its healing is to be welcomed.

The desire to attribute illnesses to psychosomatic causes is often not done in the interests of accuracy or out of concern for the sufferer, but because of difficulty with the miraculous. Equally, resistance to the idea that some illnesses are psychosomatic and healed from within is sometimes based on an undue glorification of the miraculous, or the desire to secure the miraculous as a proof of the reality of Christian faith. Both these attitudes are unhelpful complications in discerning the nature of a person's illness and leading them to greater health.

Can you think of some healings in the Bible which involve both physical and spiritual/personal needs?

DIFFERENTLY ABLED?

As recently as the mid-70s residential homes offered institutional life to young people and adults who were 'handicapped' or 'disabled'. The clear implication was that they were inferior people, not able to take any normal place in wider society. They were damaged but unhealable. Sadly these institutions were places where human dignity was not always a priority.

Today we talk of those who are 'differently abled'. We increasingly provide facilities which allow the differently abled to play a full role in society – at work, at home, in centres of recreation. There is a strong feeling that 'these people are not ill' – they simply have a different range of abilities from the norm. In particular, physical ability is not a significant criterion on which to judge human beings. Such a difference should not exclude people from society; indeed their presence reminds us that we all have different abilities and 'disabilities', and should be accepted as we are.

ILLNESS OR DIFFERENCE?

Such attitudes do not sit comfortably alongside traditional Christian approaches to healing. Accepting your limited mobility or sight – indeed embracing it as a positive characteristic of yourself – seems to run counter to Jesus' willingness to heal those diseases of his day which people accepted as 'incurable'. Lepers too were excluded from society, without any serious hope of their returning to the community. The blind and the lame became an accepted part of society as inferior people, as beggars – but Jesus changed their hopelessness into a new beginning.

But then, they asked. Many of the differently abled in our society are not asking for healing. They are asking to be accepted as they are. They are asking that we recognise their many abilities and give them the opportunity to use them.

WHAT NEEDS HEALING?

Part of what needs healing is our attitude to people who have a different set of abilities to the norm. Society needs to be healed of its intolerances – as does the Church. Perhaps healing has more truly taken place when we learn that everyone belongs and should be included.

When praying with those who are differently abled, it may be more appropriate to pray for changes in attitude amongst employers, colleagues, friends and strangers in the street. Or we might pray for them in the practical logistics of living through each day – many everyday tasks can be exhausting for them. We need to be guided by the person's own sense of what they are seeking from God. Beware of the assumption that because someone in a wheelchair is asking for prayer, their prayer will be for the restoration of their mobility. Indeed, if they come to the front of church during the time of ministry, might they not be some of the best qualified to pray for others?

Equally we need to pray with faith and hope for those who do ask for healing. We need to recognise that they are running against the culture of today, and some of their friends may see this as a betrayal of the differently abled. They will need our support as they seek to discover God's 'goodness' towards them.

A QUESTION OF IMPORTANCE

Some modern attitudes to the differently abled come close to asserting that being blind is in no way inferior to being sighted, or that being in a wheelchair is just as good as being able to walk. Thus the recent case of parents who wished to ensure genetically that their children would be born 'differently abled' like themselves.

Such attitudes may need gently to be questioned. They run the risk of turning reality on its head. But the thrust of modern thinking on 'disability' is to be welcomed from a Christian perspective. The purpose of life is God's creation of people like Himself, for a life beyond our present existence. We all need grace to look below the surface and see God's purposes being worked out.

HOW CAN I COPE WITH FAILURE?

Even those most experienced in prayer for healing find that what they pray for – even with great faith and conviction – sometimes does not happen. For those starting out on praying in this way, with faith still weak and with little experience and discernment, 'failure' is not just possible but likely. How can we live with this?

PROPER MOTIVES

As Christians we worship God alone and Christ as our Saviour. We centre our faith on the glorious redemption of the world by his painful and atoning sacrifice on the cross. Everything else, including prayer for healing, revolves around this and pales into insignificance in the face of it. But frequently, as we pursue the ministry of healing prayer, we can find ourselves subtly tempted towards the worship of the healing itself (especially when miraculous) rather than the Healer of all things, Jesus Christ.

We must examine our motives every time we pray for an ill person. Are we centred on bringing our friend's suffering before our caring Father, pleading Christ's atonement on this friend's behalf? Or are we looking for the buzz and excitement that accompanies the manifestation of the supernatural? Or indeed, are we insecure in our faith, secretly desperate for a result that will reassure us of the reality of God or of our own important place in His purposes?

Such motives are generally unconscious, but may be clearly seen by others around us. They can make the ill person uncomfortable, or even anxious for a 'result' in order to please *us*. But worse, they can stand between our friend and the healing power of Jesus. *This* is failure – failure to minister to others with a spirit of servanthood and with a genuine and holy attitude towards God. The occurrence of a significant healing – let alone an observable miracle – is in one sense wholly irrelevant. And God may be freer to grant a healing when we no longer have a personal investment in the outcome of our prayer.

OPEN MINDS

Most knowledge progresses by trial and error. We put our best knowledge into practice – and seek to learn honestly about its limitations and failures. When we refuse to accept the verdict of reality, our development of knowledge and insight goes into reverse.

The Bible speaks consistently of a God who makes Himself known in the events of life. His activity in the world today is part of His revelation of Himself and His ways. When our current understanding of His healing work seems to 'fail', then it is important to keep asking whether He is calling us forward to a better understanding, or a better way or working. This is how many people have become involved in the healing ministry – they have discovered (often to their surprise) that God is willing to work this way. We must not lose that sense of 'discovery' in relation to what actually happens in response to our prayers.

> *We may fail, but that does not make us a failure.*
> **Russ Parker**

LEARN FROM IT!

Think of a time when you prayed for someone to be healed and nothing happened. Perhaps discuss it with a friend.

- What did you think and feel before you prayed?
- What did you think and feel after you prayed?
- Why, in your opinion, did nothing happen as a result of your prayers?
- What is the most important lesson for you to learn from this incident?
- Was there anything beneficial for the person for whom you prayed?
- What will you carry with you from this, when you pray for the next person?

MEDICAL CONFIRMATION?

When we pray for someone and they appear to get significantly better, is it right to seek medical confirmation? Is it dishonouring to God to submit His work for human supervision? Or is it a right and proper check on our claims for the healing power of God at work today?

AN AFFRONT TO GOD?

Some see the pursuit of medical confirmation as bringing the work of God under worldly judgment.

- What right does any of us have to cross-question the action of God, and pass judgment on its value?

- Healing at God's hands is a mystery, a love gift to God's hurting children.

- Faith cannot be based on human proof of the miraculous. Submitting the healing ministry to public analysis can be a distraction from humble faith in the love of Jesus. We should not put God to the test in this way.

- Are doctors superior to God? Or a higher authority? Does Christianity need such professional proof?

These are real issues, and submitting a particular 'healing' for medical examination may be done from a variety of motives. We may have confidence in the work of God and be willing for any competent doctor to view it for themselves. Or we may be keen to prove to sceptical people that God's power, and therefore our ministry, is real and effective.

Jesus resisted the working of healing powers as proofs of his identity and credibility (see Matthew 12:38-41). Rather, he saw them as vehicles of the love and power of God (God's kingdom) to those who had eyes to see and ears to hear. But he was not afraid to send healed lepers to the priest to have their healing confirmed, when this was an important step in rehabilitating them back into wider society. They needed a 'clean bill of health' from the priest (acting as a kind of Public Health Officer, in accordance with the regulations in Leviticus) before they would be allowed to mix freely again.

Where there is similar good reason to look for a confirmation of a healing that appears to have happened in response to prayer, it is perhaps a necessary step of faith to allow this to happen.

A CHECK ON THE CHURCH

The Church deals in truths about things that we do not see with our eyes day by day. These spiritual truths need preserving and maintaining through the generations. But they also need to be re-examined in each generation, to see whether the way they were expressed before has now become misleading.

When Copernicus discovered that the world was round, and that it circled the sun rather than vice versa, the Church condemned him. But the way in which the church believed in God as creator needed to be challenged by new realities and new knowledge.

Similarly, our understanding of how God heals today needs to be tested by what is actually happening today in response to our prayers. This openness is important if the Christian healing ministry is going to work alongside professional health care.

NOTES

LIVING WITH QUESTIONS

Coming alongside those who are ill, whether to visit them or to pray with them, is a demanding role. It will sometimes test our 'coping' skills to the limit. It will also test our faith, as we are forced to work things out afresh amid the many conflicts and questions that arise. For all our knowledge of Scripture and our firm Christian basis of teaching, there will be much for which we have no clear answers – perhaps no answer at all. The temptation is to cover over the painful gaps with familiar religious language.

This is particularly true when people are asking 'Why?', and their thoughts turn to God. They often assume God has caused their situation, and since He is just, this must be a punishment. So the question becomes, 'Why me?' At the point of suffering and pain, there is little point in trying to instruct people better in the ways of God and the problem of evil in the world. Even such answers as there are, are of little help to us at this point.

The quiet suffering of Mary at the foot of the cross was to 'bear the pain of the unexplained'. That is the load that many seriously ill people have to bear, and part of our calling is to share that load, at least for a time.

WHOLENESS, NOT CURE

Health is a bigger concept than the absence of disease. In Christian thinking, it also includes the personal and spiritual. We are fallen people and are 'sick' in many parts of our whole person. It is often not clear what part of our person God is wanting to heal at this time. It is hard when it appears not to be the part we badly want healed! It is also sadly true that pain in one part of our person sometimes opens up healing in other parts – although it is generally far from clear how this is working in any particular situation.

When death is both the enemy and the ultimate healing, we will be left with many tensions and questions. To a society which sees physical health as hugely important, the idea of inner wholeness in the midst of suffering can seem very empty. But as Christians we must continue to believe that God wants the 'best' for us, and that this 'best' does not always include physical or even emotional healing at this point in our lives.

LEARNING, NOT RELIGION

We will also learn a lot from those without faith. This is particularly true of those who come close to death, and who seem to experience something of the spiritual world as a result. Some have an uncanny knowledge of their impending death, and even have a sense that Someone is calling them home. Others recover, and speak of experiencing something of another world. Others again seem to have spiritual insight and address their illness in the light of it.

This can be challenging to our view of the spiritual life. But it is important to work through these experiences, to learn and to grow from them, and hopefully to come to greater understanding. There is a 'mystery' about illness and death – a kind of 'holy ground'. Perhaps the essential qualification of all those who visit or pray with the sick, is their ability to tread this holy ground with sensitivity and openness. If we cannot live with questions, perhaps we need to seek out another ministry.

TRAINING TO BE A HOSPITAL VISITOR

This workbook is being made available throughout the chaplaincy system to resource the training of volunteer Visitors. This training is normally done locally by hospital chaplains, and it is likely that many chaplains will continue to do this. This workbook will be a useful resource both to them and to those they train. It will bring a greater standardisation to such training, and it gives trainees a detailed and accessible workbook to guide them in their preparation for this important role.

If you are interested in a place on the centralised course, please fill in the Enquiry Form below and send it to:

Revd Derek Fraser
The Chaplaincy
Box 105, Addenbrook's Hospital
Cambridge University Hospitals NHS
Foundation Trust
Hills Road
Cambridge CB2 2QQ

Name ....

Address ....

....

....

Postcode ....

Tel ....

I am interested in taking part in the central training course for health care visitors. Please send me further details and a booking form.

Signed ....

Date ....

Please give a few details about yourself, and why you want to train for this role.

Are you already in touch with a local hospital chaplain or a person in a similar role?

If you are a chaplain and want to order further copies of this workbook to resource your own training of Volunteers, these can be obtained at discount from:

St John's Extension Studies
Chilwell Lane, Bramcote, Nottingham NG9 3RL
Tel: 0115 925 1117

TRAINING IN PRAYER FOR HEALING

This workbook forms the basis of a national training course for those involved in prayer ministry for healing. The course has been developed jointly by the Acorn Christian Foundation and St John's Extension Studies.

The course runs by distance learning. Thee training presupposes some contact with a local church healing ministry, so candidates will need to become involved in such a ministry (either at their own church or in a nearby one) alongside other more experienced people, in order to be able to reflect on the practical aspects of this ministry.

Some churches already provide their own training for those who are going to be part of their prayer ministry teams. This workbook will be a useful resource both to them and to those they train. It will bring a greater standardisation to such training, and it gives trainees a detailed and accessible workbook to guide them in their preparation for this important role.

If you are interested in studying the module with a distance learning tutor, please complete the Enquiry Form below and send it to:

> In Search of Wholeness
> St John's Extension Studies
> Chilwell Lane, Bramcote
> Nottingham NG9 3RL

This module can be offered towards the Certificate in Christian Studies. Further details from the above address.

If you are responsible for a healing team and want to order multiple copies of this workbook to resource the training of your team, these can be obtained at discount from the above address, or from:

> Acorn Christian Healing Foundation
> Whitehill Chase
> High Street
> Bordon
> Hants GU35 0AP

Name ....

Address ....

....

....

Postcode ....

Tel ....

I am interested in studying this module with a distance learning tutor. Please send me further details.

Signed ....

Date ....

Please give a few details about yourself, and why you are interested in this.

Are you already involved in a healing ministry, either in your own church or elsewhere?